Leading with Sound

Leading with Sound is the must-have companion guide to working on video game projects. Focused on the creative, collaborative, philosophical and organizational skills behind game sound and eschewing the technical, this book celebrates the subjects most essential to leading with sound in video game development at any level. Refuting the traditional optics of sound as a service in favour of sound as a pro-active visionary department, this book examines each of the four food-groups of dialogue, sound design, music and mix, not through the usual technical and production lenses of 'how' and 'when', but the essential lens of 'why' that enables leadership with sound.

Leading with Sound is essential reading for aspiring sound designers, inside and outside of the classroom, as well as experienced professionals in the game industry.

Rob Bridgett is a British-Canadian Audio Director based in Montreal. In 1993 Rob attended Derby University to study cinema and media, and was one of the first to graduate from the 'Sound Design for the Moving Image' Master's degree programme at Bournemouth University in 1999. Having worked as an audio director in the games industry since 2001, Bridgett has become a committed advocate for 'leading with sound' and 'sound as design'.

Leading with Sound

Proactive Sound Practices in Video Game Development

Rob Bridgett

Routledge
Taylor & Francis Group

LONDON AND NEW YORK

First published
by Routledge
2 Park Square, Milton Park, Abingdon, Oxon OX14 4RN

and by Routledge
52 Vanderbilt Avenue, New York, NY 10017

Routledge is an imprint of the Taylor & Francis Group, an informa business

British Library Cataloguing-in-Publication Data
A catalogue record for this book is available from the British Library

Library of Congress Cataloging-in-Publication Data
A catalog record has been requested for this book

ISBN: 978-0-367-53590-2 (hbk)
ISBN: 978-0-367-53587-2 (pbk)
ISBN: 978-1-003-08252-1 (ebk)

Typeset in Times New Roman
by Taylor & Francis Books

Contents

Figures

Acknowledgements

This book would not exist without the inspirational conference 'Leading with Sound' organized and curated by Martin Stig Andersen, Rune Palving and John Broomhall at the Nation Film School of Denmark, Copenhagen, in October 2019. The conversations at this conference with the attendees and other participants were the inspirational spark that led directly to the writing of this book. The book would also not have been possible without the encouragement, guidance and help of Hannah Rowe at Routledge / Focal Press. I would also like to thank the poet and broadcaster Seán Street, a prolific writer about sound and the sonic imagination, for both our conversations, and simply for the inspiration to continue to write about my own experiences of sound.

Part I
Ports of entry

What is this book about?

If there is one central theme of this book, it is to help the reader to the realisation that as someone with audio expertise, you have the potential to fulfil an integral *leadership role* on any team creating a video game. This leadership especially applies in the earliest moments of a game's conceptual life, when everyone is prototyping, learning, experimenting and trying to figure out what the thing you are making *is*, who it is for and how it feels to play it.

This book is about the fundamental change in audio practice and philosophy – a change from always being at the end of production, always being the last to be thought about and applied, to instead being an active leader, and principal collaborator 'in the future' of projects – leading the way and pushing the vision forward at every step of concept, pre-production, production and, yes, still very much, post-production. With this shift comes a whole new way of seeing and thinking about the role of sound in a production. Perhaps the colonisation of post-production (an area where the majority of creative audio work *used* to happen) by other disciplines, is the reason why a lot of sound work is now migrating to the earlier parts of the production cycle. These trends of limited to no post-production time have also been bleeding from games into cinema and tv production, with the advent of real-time digital rendering and continual, rolling visual development and story changes becoming ever more fluid means that decisions and changes are *always* on the table. This very idea of a safety zone, a vantage point from which a 'locked' production can have sound and music applied to it, is now almost completely eroded, certainly on the scale at which it used to be known – so this migration includes a shift in the old certainties and expectations of *sound as a service*. This book then, is about the many areas into which sound thinking and production is now moving, to a leadership role, at the helm of the project.

Such a shift is tangible all around us, yet as sound people on-the-whole, we are not used to leading – we are used to following. Whether it is following the image onscreen, or allowing and waiting for the visions, ideas and concepts of the visual departments to provide us the fuel of influence. It is certainly a welcome opportunity, to be called on to lead, and one in which sound is in fact more than adequately armed to *excel*. Sadly, the shift isn't yet evenly distributed through the games or film industries, with many developers still operating in the older, established panic-modes of audio that they have been used to. Or, in some of the worst cases, of *expecting* sound to lead, but in reality falling back on all the old scheduling methodologies that prevent sound from being in a true leadership role, influencing the project at every level of budget and schedule, and instead forcing them into no-win crunches at the end. At the beginning of every new project, even today, we are highly likely to hear old repeated outdated and deeply-worn negative mantras about sound, from various team members across all disciplines (including sound!) that sound is always last and is always going to come in right at the end, and (with a sprinkling of optimism) save the day. Why? Where do these ideas and attitudes come from? How do they perpetuate through an industry, that I would argue from an audience standpoint, puts sound, and appreciation of that sound (and all its subcategories), on a much higher pedestal than cinema, theatre, or any other of the entertainment industries? An industry in which sound personnel are hired in a full-time, salaried capacity from the beginning of most projects. An industry which is continually, and increasingly desperate for innovation and new creative thinking. Whenever you hear these old ideas, it is an irresistible opportunity to challenge them, and to demonstrate that sound can be, and has to be, done differently. Much of this is certainly to do with the perception of sound as a discipline, from the outside, as some kind of 'black box', an invisible, intangible mystery to almost every other discipline, especially production, who simply are not used to dealing in intangibles. To most, it is vague and unclear how sound is 'manufactured', let alone ideated, conceived and applied to games, especially within the more *technically per-ceived* games industry. To an outsider, the audio field can appear to be a prickly environment, both technically and culturally a codified *insider's realm* with mysterious language, acronyms and imagery: practitioners pictured behind huge intimidating mixing desk consoles or rooms full of modular synth racks that are (often deliberately) posed to be impenetrably complex and esoteric – these are the visual codes that are continually used to signify this impenetrable and complex world of 'audio' – the message quite clear – stay out! This has to change, and it certainly starts with this book. This book is not focused on the technical or self-protecting side of sound, music or voice (or mixing! Much more of that later), it is very consciously turned away from the technical side of making sound for games. It is also deliberately turned away from those intimi-dating insider optics of exclusivity, and is very much about understanding what ideas motivate and drive audio for a general audience of game developers, students, and most definitely game audio designers and directors who feel that there is a brighter, more open, and inclusive future for the medium – one in which collaboration and exploration of creative ideas with others is *the most important thing*. For far too long, games, and especially the audio elements of games, have been defined, limited and led by the technical red lines imposed by technology. We don't need another book whose content and approaches are similarly defined and structured by the technical limits and approaches of video game sound creation, and I will try my best to avoid digging too deeply into that wherever possible. The other major problem for game audio books defined and obsessed with the technology of this medium, is that in video games, any of the ephemeral technical solutions described can only be fleetingly mastered, until quickly rendered obsolete and usurped by the coming of faster, more powerful and transparent technologies, techniques and more convenient tools and pipelines. This book then is about having and setting an 'audio vision', one freed from the shadow of technology, and how having a vision, a clear and open one, is the way in which audio really can begin to be applied. It is all about enacting a leadership role on production teams, instead of being a willing and ready tail-wagging service that simply implements someone else's vision, at the very last minute, under excruciating and unacceptable time-pressure. If a product is developed without audio, then audio becomes something that needs to be applied and resolved later. And just to be clear, by 'developed' I mean present as a visionary force at the conception and early production stages as well as leading full production and post. Audio without vision is a shameful creature living in the shadows, timidly clinging to the coat tails of the 'greater' visions of the other disciplines, able only to spread its wings and fly when told to, when allowed to, by the other departments, usually only when they have run out of fuel for visual ideas. Audio *with* vision is risen, inspired and driven to equal the other disciplines, sometimes rival them, occasionally outshine them and to tell a million more stories than those simply seen onscreen, but perhaps most essentially, it brings audiences deeply, and fully, into your worlds.

The shift in sound from a service role at the end of production, to an advance guard at the beginning of conception is a fascinating and exciting one, and it has everything to do with the change in game development from being enacted primarily as 'software development' where technology and technical redlines are the determining factors in the successful creation of a 'piece of software' – to that on an 'entertainment medium' – where the determining factors of success are defined in terms of experience and engagement of the player in the content and the game world. This requires a huge fundamental change in how developers are led, organised and managed. These shifts have been slowly taking place, as though incrementally in slow motion, over the last 15 to 20 years. Departments that simply did not exist 15 or so years ago, such as narrative and story, or user experience, have emerged and taken the reins – and sound is finding opportunities to be a part of that approach, but we need to move faster and push harder. The production periods of concept and pre-production are now, thankfully, and on many productions, much longer and more essential to the making of a successful game – and they involve almost every single discipline, rather than just technology, production, art and finance. Technology has become the means to the end, rather than the end in itself, which has in turn enabled ideas and aesthetics to lead the way.

Perhaps one of the most important aspects of sound being involved earlier, is how sound can help to realise the concept work on the earlier moments of a project inside a team. Typically, the earliest moments of a project's conceptualisation are fraught with uncertainty, failure, learning and experimentation and yet somehow, sound is often seen as a completely *dependent* service, a service that cannot even *begin* work until the uncertainties have been figured out fully – this attitude is typically why sound and music are left until much later in the process, especially if sound is relegated to a freelance service instead of an in-house full-time part of the team. However, there is huge untapped potential for sound to be an extremely agile and active participant in the development processes and culture of innovation in those early phases in particular, of concept and pre-production. Sound is quite possibly the best secret weapon for a team to have in these concept and pre-production phases. This is why the game developers who *are* leading with sound and using it in an integrated way to build and communicate their emotional experiences for their audiences from day one, are the current leaders in the video games sector, far ahead of their competition.[1] The co-founder of IDEO, Tom Kelley, in his book *The Ten faces of Innovation* [2] explains several very useful *personas,* or roles, that are critical to teams innovating – roles critical for not just dreaming up new ideas, but in implementing and delivering them. 'All good definitions of innovation pair ideas with action' – Kelley also goes on to quote the Innovation Network's definition of 'innovative employees' as 'People crafting value through the implementation of new ideas'. Of the ten personas Kelley lists, there are several which apply to audio teams and audio working in a multi-discipline game development environment very readily...

The Experimenter (Learning Persona) – *prototypes new ideas continuously, learning by process of enlightened trial and error.* This role easily fits audio in the early days of a project, as ideas and even expressions of tone and presentational identity can be quickly mocked up and played back for the team, or for test audiences. Building quick, cheap and messy prototypes of ideas and being able to identify problems with those ideas very quickly and refining them into iteratively more successful models.

The Collaborator (Organising Persona) – *helps bring eclectic groups together, and often leads from the middle of the pack to create new combinations and multi-disciplinary solutions.* This describes the role of audio as a force that reaches out to other disciplines (something it does quite naturally) and seeks to find allies with whom they can quickly work *together,* to build even more effective prototypes and experiences greater than the sum of their parts.

The Experience Architect (Building Persona) – *designs compelling experiences that go beyond mere functionality to connect at a deeper level with [player's] latent or expressed needs.* Finally, this one rings very true of what all audio should bring to a project – a *deeper meaning* for the audience – something with which they cannot just interact, but something in which they can believe and become a part of with all their heart.

Sound then is able to become the often crucially missing role in a preproduction and concept team, and help the team complete this notion of leading product development through demonstrating and conceptualising ideas, emotions and aesthetics. Sound, voice and music are incredibly easy and fast to iterate and test ideas with, whether alone, or with other departments. Sound is extremely pliable and malleable, and often requires very little in terms of time or budget to begin to experiment and try ideas out. As someone who works with sound, you have at your fingertips such an enormous amount of power to demonstrate, sketch and model ideas – grabbing material from anywhere you can find it, at even what may be considered *almost* final quality. Recording some emotive dialogue and placing some evocative sound and music cues over a series of concept images can much more fully give a sense of a game idea to team members or investors, it can bring a new team *into* the world and *inspire* – it can lead the way for the rest of production to imagine the end result. There is certainly a lot of room for everyone involved in making a game that leads with sound to imagine and dream about what the feel and look of the game would be when it is on screen – and to be inspired and excited about the direction of a game idea. This notion of continually being present to inspire and help run with ideas and get them into reality as quickly and easily as possible is fundamental to leading with sound. It is obvious to say, but sound, not being a visual medium, engages the imagination in everyone (quite certainly the best rendering engine that will ever exist), sound is able to directly go to the heart of whoever hears it and produce – in the mind's eye – the promise of a new and exciting game world or idea, from there, taking step-by-step the process of production and bringing the game onto the screen, building the world, horizontally and vertically. As production unfolds, and milestones whiz by, when the sound team reaches those final post production moments, so much knowledge and expertise is already developed about the game world being created, the story, and the emotions and contexts at every single moment in the game experienced on the controller, that the act of polishing and mixing the game, becomes one of ease and pleasure. This cannot traditionally be said of the typical models of pushing sound and all its involvement and decision making to the end of production, when all of the creative decisions have already been settled, and sound now needs to be shoehorned into fit whatever aesthetics and designs have already been deci-ded. At this late stage, sound can offer neither validation nor challenge, it just needs to fit. This is in many cases where linear audio post-production sound has been for many years. Having read about and experienced many of these frustrations with the very strict and structured post-production environ-ment of film, and film sound, taking advantage of having sound personnel on the payroll and on the project from day one in games, means that in many cases I have had the opportunity to invent and inject myself into earlier and earlier production processes on my teams. This is always to try and find opportunities where I can get involved and bring value – and to demonstrate that sound can help bring ideas to life early in the process. Worrying about throwing sound work away is never something that has bothered me as a sound designer in games, in fact it is one of the fundamentals of the work. The idea that you will be working hard on something, getting it right, and then finding out that the feature has been cut is one that is quite the every-day experience in games. You quickly learn to let go and move on, taking what learning you can from the experience and applying it to the next thing you do, building both technical and creative efficiencies all the time. This is the continual Zen-like process of acquiring a game sound designer's flexible working attitude and methodology – and it *can* take a long time to adjust to working in this world.

No maps for these territories

This book is not a guide on how to direct or make sound for games, or how to get into the industry. That is something you absolutely need to figure out for yourselves. Behind everyone who makes it into the industry is a unique portal that closes behind them, and will not open up again. This is the case for every project that you work on too. It is true that you will never take the same road or the same approach on any project, be it your first or your last. Quite simply due to the amount of variables and differences in any project at any studio, every project is of its time, and of its culture, and will be affected by the continual decisions made on that project on a day to day, hour to hour, week to week, basis by the various people and personalities on that particular team. How one person does something, is not how *you* need to approach that problem. It is extremely important to bring *yourself* to every project you work on, *you* are a vitally important dimension of the work itself.

That said, you should absolutely take as much time as you can to get to know how and why other people work on projects, trying to understand their approaches, passions, principles and perspectives. Take the things that reso-nate with you and discard the things that don't.

Being proactive in this regard, really begins with thinking. Thinking about and understanding all the exciting elements and opportunities that are possible within the sound worlds of whatever it is that you are making. Usually, the thought process for me on a project starts with imagining, exploring and becoming excited about the end result, and then reverse engineering what is required to get to that end result in terms of how the overall sound is broken up into smaller parts, what needs to drive those smaller parts, and how we, as a team, will make and improve those smal-ler parts. But it *begins* with the idea of the whole, with the imagined, complete end result. That may include music, sound and even voice, and it certainly involves a carefully and thoughtfully mixed process that commu-nicates clearly to the audience what the most important things are at any given moment. A lot of the chapters in this book discuss this central concern with *thinking about* and exploring all those interesting and per-haps under-explored areas of game sound, and how going deeper into those areas as early as possible can open up some new avenues and tribu-taries in the creative use of sound, music, voice and mix.

Notes

1 Almost every video game developer who is producing critically and commercially celebrated video games is involving audio as a deeply integrated and respected part of their development process from day one: DICE, Naughty Dog, PlayDead, Media Molecule, Ninja Theory, and Kojima Productions to name but a few prominent examples.
2 Kelley and Littman, 2005.

1 The big four

Understanding the four food-groups of audio (and how they inter-relate)

Food-groups

In order to more fully grasp and understand the enormous breadth of audio for games, and indeed audio for any media, it is necessary to break the whole subject of 'audio' down into four major food-groups, all of *equal* importance if used, that need to be thought about separately, and then also together. The purpose is not to overwhelm, but to grasp the idea of the *interconnected* soundtrack as a whole. These food groups are *sound* (designed sound effects, ambiences, Foley etc.), *music* (both score and onscreen, or source music), *dialogue* (any voice-over from characters in the scene, or voice narration from characters offscreen or disembodied voice, as well as 'Walla' crowds) and finally *mix* (not only the foreground and background choices, blending between those three food-groups at any particular moment, but any systemic or scripted mixing approaches that apply to the game such as states, ducking, volume, panning, EQ and side-chaining, as well as moments of exaggerated perspective and distance etc).

In film sound, there are often many references to the three main food-groups of voice, SFX and music, however I believe that because of the amount of complexity and time that is necessitated by game audio priority systems and interactive implementation, *the mix* should absolutely be considered as a food-group in its own right. Obviously, the mix cannot exist without at least one of the *other* food-groups, but it is such a giant and almost overwhelming and all-inclusive topic, that its importance demands at least 25% of the thinking and planning that would be accomplished on any project's audio.

We will begin then with a brief, introductory drive around some of the sub-elements and sub-neighbourhoods that are covered under each of those big four headings. What follows are some of the more traditional definitions of sound categories that you may already be familiar with.

Sound (SFX)

Within the category of sound, we will find many different subgroups. I will list and define as many as I can practically think of here, though of course there

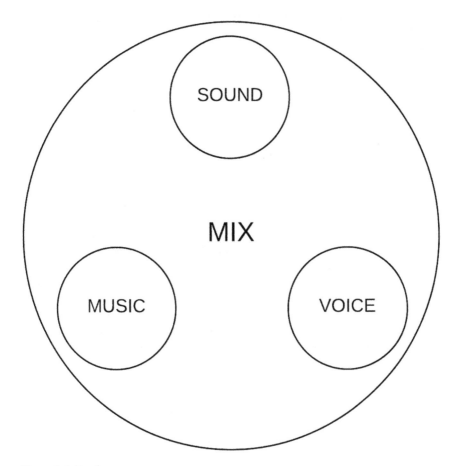

Figure 1.1 Food groups

may be many others hidden between the gaps, and hybrid groups of sound which you may consider separate as categories of their own.

Ambiences / backgrounds

In video games, ambiences have a massive range in terms of implementation and presentation, they may be static 2D or Quad ambiences that simply fade in and out as the player moves through different zones in the game. Or they may be comprised of Ambisonic sound fields or objects which similarly adapt to player and camera positioning. They may also comprise many individual single-point mono, or multichannel sounds, placed at specific locations in a map. These sounds may also be animated to move along predetermined or randomised paths to add a sense of movement and believability to an auditory scene. This category could also include dynamic sound systems that are made to cater for meteorological variables in the game, such as wind or rain, as these are often considered a part of the background ambience.

Foley

Foley[1] in games can also take on a few different meanings. The sound of *character movement* typically associated with the term Foley is often in reference to 'cloth' and 'footstep' sounds or may also be referred to as 'Moves'. These sounds may be played back in-game as part of a dynamic Foley sound system that is designed to match onscreen character or object animation, or they may be pre-designed sync sound elements that are played back as part of a cinematic cut-scene sequence. Either way, this category of sound generally refers to the movement that characters or objects make in the game *onscreen*. The term Foley in film often also includes any sounds that are made in the scene by actors, picking up objects, opening and closing doors and so on. This expansion of the category may also occur in games, with the inclusion of sound generating systems such as a physics sound system, which uses physics impulses derived from the game to play appropriately matched sounds based on material type, collision, rolling, scraping type and surface type, as well as scale. Sometimes these physics-based sound systems are also included in the definition of sync sound effects, rather than Foley. Foley can be further broken down into the Foley of the player character, or that of NPCs (non player characters), or enemy characters and animals. This separation is done so that each character type or class can be considered and implemented differently. For example, *player character* Foley may only need to be played in the centre channel at a fixed volume level, whereas enemy Foley sounds will likely need to be implemented with consideration to attenuation and filtering over distance, and 3D positioning – beyond these technical playback considerations, there will very likely be significant aesthetic and adjective-driven design differences between player and NPC Foley to consider too.

Sound effects

This often-used general term applies to sync (or 'spot') effects or specially designed effects (or FX), that have been designed and edited to match various elements of the game. It is an incredibly wide and broad category that can include entire systems such as physics collision sound, or weapon sounds (firing, handling, etc. Note: weapon handling could often be included in the Foley category too, so it is important to know that these definitions can be different based on criteria from each team or developer, and also of note that there should be no strict rules about how things are categorised). The sound effects category may also include some elements of 3D sound or weather and wind sound systems, depending very much on the kind of game being made and the environment that exists in the game as well as the genre. There may be many subcategories within this broad area, and it is essentially a catch-all category for most otherwise uncategorised sound elements.

Weapons / gear

This category will often be very deep and varied in games, depending on the amount of and customisation of weaponry and ammunition types etc. These systems can be incredibly detailed and modular, allowing deep customisation (as can be found in the 'Borderlands' games) they can also either be focussed very much on authenticity and realism (as heard in 'Battlefield' games) or they can be focussed on a POV exaggeration (sometimes also referred to as a 'Hollywood' sound) and character (as can be found in the recent 'Tomb Raider' reboot games).

UI / HUD / loading

This category is another very deep area of sound for games. User Interface (UI) and Heads-up Display (HUD) (information and menu items that are overlaid onto the screen during the game) sounds give important feedback cues to the player. Very often, menus are where a significant portion of the game play or strategic elements of game play occur. From a practical view-point, the sounds in these categories need to support information hierarchies and positive, negative selections and options as clear, immediate feedback to the player. Less pragmatically, they also need to support overall mood, and emotional values of the game, that still feels like the player is part of the world of the game. I would also include in this category any loading sounds or loops that are needed to bridge the experience of the game from main menu interfaces to gameplay, and back again, or between levels, chapters or zones.

Music

Within the music category, there are a few different types of music to consider. Though not exhaustive, here are some of the ones which are currently the most prominent and commonly used in games.

Score

This category refers (mostly) to the original music that is written to accompany the game. Score is typically considered non-diegetic, meaning that its sonic source is not located within the scene or 3D world that the player is seeing onscreen. It is generally understood that the score represents the emotional state of the characters, player or world itself, and therefore lends the experience a 'cinematic' aesthetic, having borrowed this form of musical accompaniment from film and theatre. A score can consist of linear segments to accompany sync cinematics or canned action or dialogue sequences, and it can be inter-active, or generative depending on the kind of gameplay system and feedback it is there to support. The music can be produced in stereo, or in quad, or surround 5.0 or 7.0 formats, or more recently spatial audio formats such as Ambisonic sound-field recordings or pre-designed and panned sound-fields. A score may also migrate between non-diegetic and diegetic representation (for example transitioning and panning from the non-diegetic '2D' score, to playback through a '3D' radio source object in the game world), and it may also move around the player in 'non-diegetic space' (a 3D acoustic space that exists for the score, but not contiguous with the 3D game space onscreen). It is also generally safe to assume that the characters in the 3D world cannot hear the music of the score, and therefore cannot react to hearing it, because it represents a layer of emotion somewhere between the main character and the player themselves. The score is very often made by a composer specifically for the game, though it is not entirely unheard of to have scores adapted, in part, from pre-existing music.

Licensed music

Not all music for games will be specifically composed for that game, and pre-existing music may certainly be licensed for synchronisation in a particular title. There are a couple of different kinds of licensed music that might occur, the first would be licensing of pre-existing recording to appear in the game, whether that is played on fictionalised radio stations in the game world, as in the Grand Theft Auto series, or similarly, the many electronic music tracks that were licensed to play in Wipeout – these are often pre-existing songs by artists that are already fairly recognizable by the target audience.

The second kind of music licensing, is the licensing of music to be used as a score – music that can be licensed and then re-edited to work in an interactive manner that fits the feedback required for the player in the game. Some nice examples of this kind of library music use can be found in the Little Big Planet series from developer Media Molecule.

Source music

Source music is that which emanates from a physically present, or implied, source in the 3D world of the game itself, for example, radio, television speakers, or musicians performing in the game world. This is music that the characters themselves can 'hear' and react to. Source music often follows the 3D rules of panning and attenuation that other 3D sound effects in the game world follow, such as high-pass filtering over distance, and reduction in volume when the listener moves further away from the source. Source music will also inhabit and excite the reverb of the diegetic space onscreen and be considered as more of a sound effect than it is considered as music. Different games treat source music quite differently; Grand Theft Auto for example is known to have lots of source music play through its radio stations, and these tracks are experienced as direct stereo music that doesn't pass through the diegetic world in the same way that other sound effects do, this is to emulate playback as though you were listening on headphones or to a car stereo from a first person listener perspective, rather than matching the third person perspective of the camera, which while perhaps more realistic, would not be as exciting, immersive or engaging. Source music can be either specially composed for the game by a composer or can be pre-existing licensed music. As mentioned already, it has also been known to be included in the broad category of 'sound effects' – especially in the categorisation that is used in the sound options menu settings for adjusting the volume levels of different elements of the game (music, sound, dialogue) –undoubtedly because the music is diegetic and part of the game world's soundscape, rather than score which is non-diegetic. The inclusion of source music in the environmental reverb system, would probably also have much to do with this, as well as the fact that characters in the world may 'hear' or be reacting to these sources of music heard in the world itself.

UI stingers

An additional element of musical scoring that is not necessarily considered as part of the game world itself, is the use of musical stingers as elements of feedback in the User Interface. Many games use musical stingers to emotively re-enforce and give feedback on options that are being chosen and navigated by the player inside the menu. While these elements may be linked to the narrative, they can constitute a continuation of some of the 'score' of the game and play into the notion of keeping the player immersed in the emotional world of the game while navigating the menus and changing game settings, particularly if some subtle under-scoring is used in the *background* of these menus. It is important to remember that sometimes these musical score-like stingers attached to actions in the menus are the only sonic element providing feedback to the player about menu selections (meaning there is no *additional* sound effect), and that these sounds would ideally be categorised as 'sound effects' in the sound option settings, thus changing the music slider volume levels, would perhaps have no effect of the levels of the volume of these musical UI stingers. So this is often an area of some confusion and certainly a grey area of sound categorisation – it must also be noted that much of the time these stinger elements are edited and created, not *by* the composer as part of the musical score of the game, but more often by a sound designer, chopping out elements of the musical score and re-appropriating them as UI 'sound effects'.

Voice

An element of increasing aesthetic importance and nuance in video games over the past 30 years is voice. There are a great many ways to incorporate and consider voices in games, and this category has a variety of functions and meanings from simple feedback, or mission contextualisation to emotional performance. There are many major elements of voice to consider as a part of this food-group.

Narration or voice-over

A *non-diegetic* voice-over is one present in the soundtrack and conveying story, narrative or gameplay context to the audience. This is typically an imitation of the role of a narrator in cinema, television, radio or theatrical productions, in that it is a framing device for the storytelling (often the voice of a character looking back over events that have already happened, or narrating the story of their own experiences).

Onscreen character dialogue (diegetic, spoken with lip-sync)

This type of voice is from characters that exist in the game world, who will speak and converse with one another or with the player. The dialogue they speak is written as part of narrative or dialogue systems, which takes into account a variety of contexts and logic states and plays the appropriate dialogue line or response usually from the 3D position of the character that is speaking. These diegetic voices often make increasingly sophisticated use of either generative lip-sync (lip-sync or mouth-shape and mouth flap of the character model driven by the wave data of the dialogue files being 'spoken') or even accompanying facial capture data that is taken from the actor delivering the lines at the same time they are recorded in the studio for even more precise performance fidelity.

Offscreen character voice-over (radio, telephone and other voices)

Another type of voice that often occurs in video games is the non-diegetic 'inner voice' or 'inner thoughts' of the player or central character being made audible as voice-over in the game. One notable example of this being Remedy Entertainment's 'CONTROL' in which the central character, right from the beginning of the game, has their inner thoughts rendered as speech to the player so we can hear what she is thinking as well as hearing what she is saying out loud in the game world. This is, again, a convention that is taken from cinema and radio to give the player information, via voice, about the inner thoughts of the character we are hearing. Other examples of off-screen character voice are commonly heard via 'radio' conversations from characters in the diegesis, who are in distant locations. It is very common in games to have a companion character who is able to help the player by guiding them or giving them information remotely via radio, without needing to be in the same location.

Barks

This category of sounds (also referred to as AI driven dialogue or NPC systemic dialogue) is often used in open-world games or combat heavy games, where characters, most often NPC, have large quantities of variations of a particular kind of dialogue response (for example 'get hit' or 'find cover') which match a specific kind of reaction or move that the NPC is making.

These variations of the same kind of reaction give more depth and authenticity to what is a highly *repetitive* event trigger occurring over and over again in potentially many different contexts throughout the entire game. This could be adding 20 to 30 different ways of saying 'Grenade!' when throwing a grenade toward the player, or up to 100 different ways of saying 'Great job!' when returning to complete a mission from a persistent mission-giver character.

This category could also be expanded to consider things like background conversations between characters, those overheards that often play randomly in the background to create the illusion that characters are having a conversation. These lines usually contain sometimes relevant or minor story detail, or reflect the current general *state* of the story, meaning that, unlike in cinema, a player could spend quite some time listening and getting useful information or background colour detail from these overheard conversations. These background lines are likely to be 'ducked' (more on this later in the mix section) in the mix whenever a more important or significant player or story line of dialogue plays at the same time.

Walla

As an extension of the idea that the general sound of background chatter in the world is necessary to add convincing colour and believability to the game's crowd environments, walla is a category borrowed from film and radio sound which is often categorised more as an ambience *sound effect* element than a *dialogue* element. Unlike background conversations, the words in walla are indiscernible and tend to just give a hint at a mood of background chatter content. Walla 'moods' can be many and varied in certain locations precisely to accommodate the dynamic changes in moods of larger crowds of people (examples: calm, relaxed, angry, or terrified crowds) as well as adjusting and representing the different sizes of crowds either shown or implied on screen (small, medium, large, vast etc). As mentioned, this is often categorised as a sound effect when it comes to the setting volume in the sound options menu.

Grunts / efforts

This category of voice refers to the nonverbal sounds made by characters as they exert themselves physically in the world, each category consisting of many variants so as not to feel repetitive when re-triggered over and over again. These sounds can be the most triggered and most often heard in any game, and therefore often require the most variants per category (jump, land, punch) but also the most variety of *categories* with which to more exactly match the exertions of the characters on screen. The amount of efforts and grunts of a main player character will often far outweigh those made for NPCs, simply because the main character will perform a richer variety of moves and navigation, and be onscreen for the entire game, but also because enemy NPCs or pedestrian support characters will not have anywhere near the depth of action or onscreen time that can be performed to support their animations. A lot of the time, efficiencies will be used to avoid recording too many of these kinds of lines to avoid having actors destroy their voices with long and intensive shouting and grunting recording sessions – and this category of voice sounds has come under the scrutiny of voice acting unions for this very reason.

Mix

This fourth food-group is all about considering how the *previous* three food-groups interrelate and interact with one another. With increasing processor power and memory bandwidth, as well as efficient and lossless decoding of compressed sounds, the fidelity and *amount* of sounds that can be played back at any one time in a game engine drastically increased in the generational jump between the PS2 and the PS3, or Xbox and Xbox360 (around 2005–2006). This made games that simply had no strategic runtime mixing approach or prioritisation culling methods applied to their sound engines extremely cacophonic and messy. With that generational transition came the increased need for dynamic mixing systems and priority systems which were able to cull and control the amount of sounds being played back at any one time, and these approaches further led to a much more 'cinematic approach' to mixing, that of deliberately limiting and choosing what was the most important element at any one time (a quite dynamic and complex pro-blem when considering both the gameplay systems, and the narrative contexts in which those systems are occurring). It helps if you think about game mixing as the 'dynamic priority of what the player needs to hear', rather than 'mixing' in any traditional film sound sense, because the mix of a game is about so much more than the relative volume of the sounds, or categories of sounds – it includes the *dynamic* relationships between those categories.

Passive, automated mixing systems

Side-chaining

This is one of the most commonly used automated mixing techniques in games, whereby the signal from one bus – for example, the main dialogue bus – is used to attenuate downwards the levels of another bus (or busses) – for example, the music bus – in order to create a priority system whereby the voice is dynamically taking priority in the mix by reducing the volume level of the music in the game as it plays. The important thing about side-chaining is that it will 'read' the incoming dialogue levels of the dialogue bus and apply those to the music bus in real-time, so if louder dialogue occurs, then the music can be typically reduced more or less according to how you wish to set it up. Of course, there are a variety of ways that these signals can interact with the target bus, but generally it is used to dynamically duck down the volume level. Specific frequency targeting in more sophisticated side-chaining can be done by *only* attenuating the frequencies of the music bus that are being *used* by the dialogue bus, therefore not creating a crude overall volume reduction, but just the reduction of frequencies of the music track often around the 1,000khz range. This method is useful for a more transparent mix effect and avoids a pumping 'compressed' feeling in the signal being reduced, particularly in the low-end of music tracks.

Ducking

Ducking is a less sophisticated but more processor efficient version of side-chaining, that is often used to carve out big volume reductions without the need to be continually processing and reading the incoming signal and applying it to the target signal. It is a far less subtle effect, of turning down the target signal or bus by a pre-specified amount, for example -6dB, every time any signal is detected in the main source bus.

Attenuation curves (filtering and volume over distance)

Setting up the amount of volume, low pass or high pass filtering that occurs on a 3D object's sound as the listener in the game gets further away from the sound source, is called attenuation, and is often expressed (in middleware platforms like Audiokinetic's Wwise) via something called 'attenuation curves'. These curves allow a great deal of finessed control over how sound is filtered over distance to convey the feeling that it is close or far and communicate this information back to the player. Each curve represents a particular parameter, such as volume over distance, high pass filter over distance, reverb amount over distance, high pass filter over distance and so on. There are the possibilities to define a whole variety of different attenuation curves based on the priority of the different groups of sounds used in a game. Important story critical dialogue lines that need to be audible over much greater distances in a 3D environment will have attenuation curves that do not fall-off in volume as quickly, and less important background lines of NPC conversational dialogue, for example, will have attenuation curves that fall-off more quickly and perhaps more realistically.

Active override mixing systems

Snapshots / States

These are snapshots settings of fader levels for a variety of busses, that can be installed by the game to coincide with a particular event, for example when pausing the game. When the game is paused, we may want to set all the 3D in-game sound busses to -96dB so that they are no longer audible. Therefore, as this snapshot, or state, is installed and uninstalled, the volumes are for those groups of sounds are set and reset accordingly. There is often also a crossfade time setting that is applied to snapshots which tells them how long to take to get from where the current value snapshot is, to the newly introduced target value on the new snapshot, so from 0dB to -96dB perhaps over the time of two seconds, will result in the sounds on that bus fading down from full volume to silent over that amount of time. Snapshots usually handle many values at the same time for many sound objects (either entire *groups* of sounds buses, or individual sounds), and also can handle multiple types of sound attenuation, such as filtering, pitch, reverb amount, and auxiliary send values, as well as volume.

Transitions

At their simplest, transitions could apply to the amount of time taken to fade the volume levels from one pre-set state to another – but transitions also come into play when you are moving from one zone to another in the game, or from the in-game soundscape to that of the menu or the map screen. Transitions always need to be thought about in terms of how the various elements of the soundtrack will be treated. Transitioning from pre-rendered cut-scenes to in-game systemic sound is one particular challenge that still trips up many developers in handing off pre-rendered sound to runtime sound. Transitioning geographically (to highlight an objective that is miles away from the player's location), or temporally (via flashbacks or flash-forwards in the narrative) can similarly present very difficult challenges for the soundtrack and run-time sound engine, especially if it is largely built on systems which did not anticipate such storytelling techniques. If your goal is to have all the sound in the game appear smooth and continuous, then transitions will be the point at which you have the most technical challenges – very often what goes on behind the scenes in terms of loading or streaming is antithetical to the notion of smooth continuous sound, and various sound elements, such as a short preloaded transition sound effects, or fading up and down a short loop of ambient sound during a loading sequence, can help to hide and make these elements *appear* polished and smooth for an audience, rather than having sound suddenly cut-out completely when a loading screen (and loading process) is suddenly invoked. Mapping out and planning ahead for things like loading, in terms of sound, as early as possible, is prudent in terms of being able to anticipate the technical challenges with these architectural elements of how the game is built – but always maintaining the perspective of the player's experience. Maintaining control over all the elements of the soundtrack at such transition moments is incredibly important in video games as they themselves transition from software to entertainment.

Platform / hardware endpoints

Given all of this content, the game you are making may be playable on a variety of mix endpoints. An endpoint is a term used to describe both the *device* (like a console, or computer) used to deliver the mix of all the sounds to the consumer, and the output configuration. If you are working solely on a PlayStation or Xbox exclusive title, you still have quite a few endpoints to consider, from stereo TV speakers, to spatial or stereo headphones, to surround speaker home theatre. If you are working on a cross-platform title, that can be played on either Sony or Microsoft's platforms, you now have a very dense cluster of endpoints to support, in essence some of them may share similarities (spatial headphone mixes on Microsoft and Sony platforms may not differ too much in terms of how they are implemented and mixed), yet all still require support, testing and down-mix consideration. So, having a view of all the supported endpoints, and also a plan to address the mix of those endpoints during a mastering pass, *derived* from a master mix, is ever important as the diversity of those endpoints increases over time.

Note

1 Foley is a term named after the film sound artist, Jack Donovan Foley (1891–1967), who was a pioneer in many early film sound techniques.

2 What drives the mix of your game?

Because we are thinking of the mix as the 'dynamic priority of what the player needs to hear' this actually means that you, the person who is in charge of making this happen onscreen, need to know the answer to that question, at every moment in the game before you can construct and script the 'mixing systems' to realise that vision at runtime. You may not know the answer to these questions at first, and that is quite normal, because this is something that you will learn as you build the game together with the rest of the team. As you do this and talk to different groups within the studio working on the game, the notion of what the most important thing is will change. The design team may say the right kind of player feedback is the most important, while the creative director may say the emotion is the most important. The animation team may tell you the Foley that is synced with the animation system is the most important, and so on. At first this can be very frustrating, but this is a necessary education in video game sound when eventually you are able to think about what is important to the *audience* and not the developer. However, it is just as important and essential to consider that different players will have different priorities and ideas about what the most important information is for them in *their* game experience – this can be taken into account by providing control over volume levels, or dynamic range compression, in the user's audio options. In fact, it is essential to be able to encourage a meaningful portion of mix decision making into the preference of the players themselves, but in a way that is easy to access and with categories of sound that make sense for each specific game. You can still author the default overall mix decisions about the experience based on perhaps an 'idealised player', however, these notions need to be overridable by your diverse audience. Here is an area in which video games have made more progress (though there is still much work to do) over and above the world of home entertainment in film sound for example.

We need once again to re-assert here that games are 'entertainment'. Games can be played anywhere, in any acoustic environment. Games can be played by anyone, from any demographic, or socio-economic background. They can be played on any supported device, and through any connected audio system it is possible to conceive of. An approach to a mix that presupposes that the player is listening in as perfect an environment as the one you mixed the game in, and therefore should be only the 'one mix' that the audio team has 'sanctioned', is an ignorant one built on a privileged perspective and unawareness of the scale and scope of your audience. In this sense, the mix cannot ever be called 'final' because it should always be in the hands of the consumer to make those final decisions about the priorities of the main sound categories and dynamics at their individual endpoint, based on their preferences and playback circumstances. The term 'Master Mix' may be used here instead of 'Final Mix' in this case, as it implies that the developer has authored a quality-sanctioned *master* default mix, per platform endpoint, but which can then be further tweaked to an individualised *final* endpoint by the player.

Personalised endpoints

The idea of *individual* endpoints is one that complements nicely the idea of the platform endpoints, because it presupposes that the consumer has a vast range of dynamic environmental and psychological endpoints in their lives, and that the mix will potentially need to be further adjusted and tweaked to meet the shifting sands of those individual needs. To add to this, accounting for the psychical and biological differences for every individual player with new technologies like personalised HRTF measurements – we are seeing a more inclusive, diverse and accessible future for the entertainment that we make.

Hearing impairments and cognitive processing disorders also take a variety of forms, and with the demographics of gamers getting increasingly older, it is more likely that a hearing impairment or trauma may affect those playing your title. Again, these audiences are *not fixed*, but dynamic, hearing impairments may develop and become progressively worse for one player, similarly, cognitive processing disorders may increase or be lessened over time due to any number of anxieties or therapies, which would further necessitate the need for user-adjustment of the mix in your games.

Understanding and acknowledging all of these different areas and categories is incredibly important in order to be able to build a picture of the *experience of the player*. It is important to have both an aesthetic idea and also a plan of execution for each of the three content food-groups, and especially a plan to be able to mix all those content groups in relation to one another (the mix food-group – which I think of as the 'contextualisation' food-group). But it is also extremely important to understand the various mastering tweaks needed for the platform endpoints in terms of down-mixing, as well as accommodating the existence of dynamic individual endpoints (user sound options) via meaningful user mix options. It may not be at the top of your mind at the beginning of a project, but at a time where audio typically is not engaged in producing polished final assets, there is certainly scope and time to be able to start sketching out and researching these areas much earlier than you might be used to. There very well may be technology to build and pipelines to put in place to accommodate these features, and there most certainly will be people in other disciplines to talk to about all these ideas, so start thinking about this early.

3 Taking a psychological approach to sound categorisation

All these food-group categories and sub-categories are listed here in somewhat objective production groupings, and they assume the hierarchical relationships to the broad categorisations that we would entirely expect when producing them. However, when we are leading with sound, directing the overall experience, and especially when considering the dynamic elements and changes of those elements over time in our games, this production-centric categorisation becomes superseded by an even higher level categorisation of all of these same sounds, one based not on what *production group* they belong to, but one based on a *psychological* grouping. This higher-level categorisation of sounds, beyond their functional and production labels, enables us to think deeper about the creative meaning and organisation of sounds, and especially about the *transformation* of the sound, music and dialogue in a game over time.

Two realms of sound

One distinction that is often not apparent when working with presenting sound onscreen, is that we continually deal with two streams of sound events, the tangible and the intangible, material and non-material, or to put it another way – sounds from the objective observable reality onscreen, and sounds from the imaginative and interpretive point-of-view. Sounds that spring from and represent the 'inner emotions or intellect' of characters, or indeed players. These two sources of sound events, and their crossover territories, underlie many of this book's investigations into the subject of leading video game development through sound, and of the fundamental importance of understanding these two originating forces of sound *before* being capable of fully exploring the conceptual and production process of developing games through experiments in sound, music, voice and mixing. These two sources, of *tangible* real sounds, involving simulated sound systems that find observable inspiration in the natural world and, of *imagined* psychological sound, filtered, interpreted (also misinterpreted) and exaggerated sound, came up a lot more than I thought they would when I set out to write this book. Not only this, but they appear to underpin many of the creative avenues of sound that most excite our imaginations, and engage our audiences in much deeper ways, within *every* food-group of sound. Perhaps most interestingly, in almost every game I have worked on, and played, it is possible to point to an area where these two sources of sound events intermingle and become unclear, in a place *between* the diegetic and the non-diegetic. In games, again perhaps more so than in cinema or any other audio-visual media, this is a vast, elastic ambiguous space, a highly *interpretive* space, within which there is no clear separation between whether what we hear has a cause in the material world onscreen, or is emanating from and *through* the inner interpretative filters supplied by the character's, or *player's* (in the case of many *first-person* perspective video games) imagination and interpretive filters. The more sound design is led by storytelling, and directed by adjectives, the more of this latter interpretive sound we end up presenting to the audience, and the more we leave behind the sonic 'facts' of the events themselves. This, in favour of presenting a form of exaggerated shadow sound. When we speak of realism in sound for games, we are most often referring to *psychological* realism, the *feeling* of firing a gun, and all the accompanying psychology that sits behind the mind that pulls the trigger, not the real sound of the gun, or the car engine, or the cave drip itself.

Third wave game sound

John Broomhall, at the 'Leading with Sound' conference opening keynote in Copenhagen, 2019, made a very relevant and thoughtful observation that has great relevance here. That, in the early beginnings of game sound, the problem we were trying to solve was *What sound is it possible to play?* In John's words, 'What does the player need to hear?' Almost entirely limited by technology, the question for sound designers, programmers and developers was literally, what are we *capable* of playing? In a subsequent secondary phase of game sound, an advancement away from severe technical limitations and into more simulation based systemic sound approaches, perhaps exemplified by titles like Battlefield, we now asked the question *What sound is it possible to hear?* In John's words, 'What can the player theoretically hear?' And as a result, a great deal of the thinking and technology development was pointed into the direction of modelling the sound based on what was perceivable by human ears in 'reality' using physics and perceptual biology as the driving inspiration.

To pick up and continue Broomhall's thread, in the *next* tertiary (third wave) of the development of sound thinking in games, the technical and aesthetic ambition in games is now one looking into the inner psychology of characters and players, and away from the objective real world possibilities of sound physics. Instead we are now becoming more preoccupied with storytelling and psychological sound, perhaps with more aesthetic kinship to the cinema that many sound designers so often find themselves admiring – *Eraserhead, Apocalypse Now, The Conversation* etc. As we enter this third phase of sound enquiry we must now ask… *What sound is it possible to imagine?* This final question reverses the notion that sound in games is being driven and framed by technology and systems, or indeed by simulation of an objective reality, but now we can begin to explore what our characters or players *imagine* they hear, and how sounds are filtered through the personality and psychology of the inhabitants of our worlds. Our creative process of exploring sounds on screen begins not with the idea that we need to physically simulate everything about the real world, but can first ask what is the sound of the inner world of a character's point-of-view? Of course, not every game goes all the way into this definition, and indeed many games offer interesting mixes of both sounds that could occur and be heard objectively by a player or player character, and also of sounds which include some significant cinematic design in which sounds are exaggerated and played much larger than life, pushing a more psychological perspective on the sounds mediated to the audience. But we certainly now have the capability and possibilities to *choose* what approach our game needs – which dimension to present to our audience, and perhaps ask how to blend between these many realities.

Any categorisation of sound must take into account a dynamic model of presenting sound to the player that considers these categories, especially in terms of timing and sequencing. We need to consider the full spectrum of perceptual phenomena that takes into account the purely objective, as well as the purely emotional and personal. Is a sound that is played in your game, objective, intellectual, or emotional? If you can answer these questions, then you are likely able to think about and apply that to all the food-groups and the mix of the game, on an entirely different level. One which gives a more overarching thought to the entire audio vision, as well as helping to clarify the mix delivered to the audience.

In order to understand what sound should or should not play, when, and in what sequential order those sounds should be 'heard' (experienced) by the player, we may need to apply this additional context and categorisation of character psychology. A simple way to talk about this, is to ask, 'What is the player or main character feeling in this moment?' Knowing what this additional context is can be very helpful in being able to lead discussions with sound, because knowing psychologically what is going on in the game is probably the only way you will understand what is *really* the most important sound (rather than what person or department x, y or z on the team tells you is the most important sound), at any given moment, and the only way you will understand the why is from a psychological storytelling perspective. Having these conversations with the team is crucial and is extremely revealing. Why is the reverb for a particular space much bigger than the space itself? Why is it more important to hear and focus on certain sounds in that reverberant environment in that particular moment? Why do we need to hear the echoey memory of a voice from the past at this precise moment of the game? Putting all this onscreen is not without its challenges. Exaggerating something like reverb could be interpreted by the QA (Quality Assurance) department as a bug (an unintentional side-effect of something not being set-up correctly), but if it is part of the storytelling design so that the player/audience can feel an emotionally different way about the space, then it needs to be communicated, ideally ahead of time, to the QA department and even better, to every department. Navigating the fine line between something feeling like a broken or unintentional part of the game and a deliberate artistic choice, is very demanding and will often be easier to 'sell' to an audience if there are also visual accompaniments to signal some difference in perception. All of this requires time, lots of experimentation and iteration as you will likely be going against standard audience expectations.

Here are some further ways of re-categorising and thinking about sound from different causal and psychological places in games.

World, heart, mind

Objective sounds (world)

Sounds that we can expect to be heard in the diegetic game world that other characters in that game world will also hear. Example: An active Pile Driver seen on a construction site in the game, we expect to hear the deafening, metallic, anvil-like hit each time the pile-driver drops. Another example would be character footsteps, or indeed anything that is seen onscreen and expected to produce a sound as a way of *grounding* those elements into reality. Reverberation and environmental effects can also be considered as objective, by matching the reflections we would expect to hear in a space of roughly that size and shape and material, reflectivity and so on. A lot of sound designers go to extraordinary lengths to make these kinds of simulations feel as convincing as possible. Though it should be noted that the human brain is very well used to reverberation not quite matching what we see – as in the case of caves, we may only be able to provide the brain with a tiny amount of visual information from what we can *see*, when in fact what we *hear* tells us that the materials and the space of the cave, goes on for much further than we assume from those visual cues.

Emotional sound (heart)

Sounds emanating from, or framed and highlighted by, the emotions of a character – these sounds might provide emotional revelations about a character's inner feelings or life and they may be in contradiction to what we see. As an example: We see a confident businessman in a busy office talking on the phone continuously, but all the while the background sound is sparse and we only hear the intimate sound directly in the space of our main character, we do not hear the bustling busy office around him, telling us that all the while, the person we see is deeply isolated and alone, perhaps yearning for, but unable to find, more direct human connection. This could also be achieved with diegetic voice – an emotional spoken reaction in dialogue (less scripted, acted in more improvised sentences... with hesitation and repetition, perhaps feeling like an emotional outburst) – all this sound exists to help us understand that this is coming from the *heart* of the character. Or it could be non-diegetic speech, daydreaming thoughts occurring inside the characters head that we, the audience, are able to hear. Musical score very often also fulfills this brief too, by conjuring the mood, feeling and emotion of the inner emotional reality of a character. Similarly, reverb can be exaggerated to be emotional in that it amplifies what we see on screen to make it even more metaphorically powerful, be that a larger more empty feeling (Charles Foster Kane, alone in his Xanadu Mansion in 'Citizen Kane') or a claustrophobic tight cave crevasse (as in Shadow of the Tomb Raider's opening cave crawl-up sequence which uses mono reverb and sound all panned into the centre channel only).

Intellectual sounds (mind)

Sounds emanating from, or framed and processed by, the intellect of a character – this most often applies to vocal expression that characters make, and their tight control over their emotions – showing the intellectualisation and control of emotions and events through sound – a good example of this is the dialogue spoken by a character to explain their actions in a rational way, or as rational and emotionless reactions to events in the world. These sounds often hide or mask the deeper repressed emotions of a character – the sound in a scene may be orchestrated by a character in order to produce an effect on people coming into their space for the first time. We may have a villain who has set up a space with a specific piece of music playing in the background, perhaps some opera or classical music to suggest sophistication. This mise-en-scène may all be arranged to manipulate visitors, to impress them in some way, or lure them into a false assumption.

Of course, a sound may begin its onscreen life as one of these elements and then transition to become another, perhaps through changing the reverb subtly throughout a scene as the emotional context changes. By hearing an abstract, distant sound that we cannot see, we may hear just the emotional interpretation of that sound that our character onscreen feels, the distant sound deliberately warped, designed and changed to sound strange and eerie in order to reflect the fear in our character – as we dynamically get closer and reveal the source of the sound – revealed and robbed of both its distance and of its transformative and blurring reverberation and echo, it may simply be a mundane element that we can henceforth easily identify like sheet of metallic roofing blowing in the wind. This dynamic vector of sounds, music cues and voices through the different categorisations of perception (world, heart, mind) should certainly be considered broadly, from a game engine or implementation perspective, as world simulation or storytelling – but wherever you can, your systems need to be able to adapt to carry sounds through these metamorphoses and these blending psychological viewpoints.

Transitional zones

While well-defined categorisations are useful, they are not hard borders which you cross into and switch from one mode of perception to another, and often there is considerable bleed between these categories. Sometimes these transitionary zones are vast, and sometimes they are brief. Understanding that the cause and reception of every sound is dynamic, and that the context changes each time the sound may be heard is key to developing systems and methods by which sound can be changed and modified through an ever-changing perceptual lens. Mix states and parameters are great methods to achieve some of this technically, as are blending and crossfading between different versions of the same sound – but again, understanding *why* those sounds need to be dynamically changed is the only way that you can lead this creation process and have the correct states prototyped and tested, and the right supporting technology scripted, prioritised and deployed on your development team.

A piece of source music can start to play on a radio in a 3D environment from a single point in space (diegetic) filtered to match the type of radio speaker, having the reverb of that space modelled accurately and convincingly to what we see with our eyes. Then, a slow transition can occur whereby the music blends gradually, almost imperceptibly into a non-diegetic direct 2D stereo sound, which plays now full-bandwidth with no speaker processing, and takes on a more emotional commentary, matching a character's mood as that character reacts freely and openly to the music – or even an intellectual resonance by showing a character making very deliberate, choreographed, precise and rehearsed actions to that music – a villain's routine enacted, rehearsed and set to music.

4   What is a game developer?

Understanding what a game developer actually is, from the inside, is fundamental to comprehending where game audio really fits in and what our potential leadership role might be. If we simply define a game developer as a business or economic unit, this does not tell us where we might fit in from a collaborative perspective. For the purposes of this book, where we are looking specifically at ways in which sound is capable of leading the creative and development process from inside a project, we will look at and define game developers quite specifically as *collaborative collectives of individuals, teams and disciplines*. We will also look at the way these disciplines can scale up and down and how they might interact as they do so. Arguably, a game developer could be an entity that exists without any economic purpose at all. When we talk about game development studios, and game developers, we all assume we know what a game developer is... a company that is formed to create games (usually seen as 'software'), for money, using technology to build them. We also, from a high level, generally might assume this could be either 'triple A' or 'Indie' – two labels that the industry still uses to delineate the large budget production from the smaller budget production entities. In truth, these labels don't tell us much at all about the kinds of games or entertainment experiences that these companies are making. It is generally accepted that an indie studio, makes smaller-scale games, and a Triple A studio typically makes larger scale games – however this doesn't always stack up when you think about the astonishingly vast scale of a game like 'No Man's Sky' made by a very small indie developer Hello Games. It is also quite interesting to note that both the term 'indie' and 'triple A' have become almost *styles* of entertainment products for example – having an 'Indie aesthetic' or Triple A 'production values'. One could perhaps define an *indie aesthetic* if one excludes the business model and team size of the studio that made that game, likewise it is slightly redundant to describe a *game* as triple-A in terms of quality (as evidenced by so many games titles described as triple-A with huge budgets, but receiving mid to low review aggregate scores on the quality of the game experience). So, here at least, we will try to define a game developer by what is going on inside it.

Discipline scale

Game developers are made up of disciplines[1] and those disciplines scale up or down depending on projects and requirements of those projects by using teams or departments.

I have developed a way of looking at game developers from a disciplinary scale perspective, which is especially useful when thinking about the type of team and the type of game that is being produced. The important thing to note here, is that if the size and complexity of the other departments is unbalanced, say we have a massive art and animation team with several layers of management and leadership embedded not only inside the game team, but also a wider global leadership for art and animation across multiple projects at the studio level (keeping an eye on innovation and defining overall quality)... yet, if that same kind of hierarchy is not to be found in the audio department, then there is little chance for audio to be able to lead – as they will be spread too thinly and essentially in fire-fighting mode the entire time trying to keep up with the massive lists of sounds being generated by all those art assets. In fact, each departmental discipline in each studio, at every scale, should ideally be balanced in scale and scope. Together then, these disciplines will reflect the type and scale of game that is being made.

Serizawa scale

I am using, for the purposes of entertainment, the Serizawa scale, which is taken from the movie Pacific Rim (and actually named after the lead scientist in the original Godzilla movies). It is an exponential scale which describes the size and threat of a Kaiju (monster) in the movie. This is simply to make the point more playful and memorable and is not meant in any way to suggest that these development teams are deadly or dangerous in any way. The model I am using here considers only the big five overarching disciplines of Audio, Art, Design, Code and Production. While there are also Animation, Marketing, QA, UX, UI and many other sub-disciplines such as VFX, that *could* be included, I have chosen these big broad categories to represent those other disciplines just for the ease of illustrating the point.

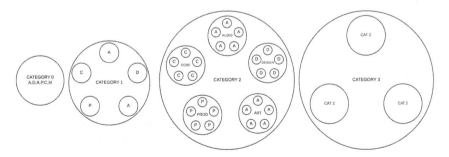

Figure 4.1 Serizawa

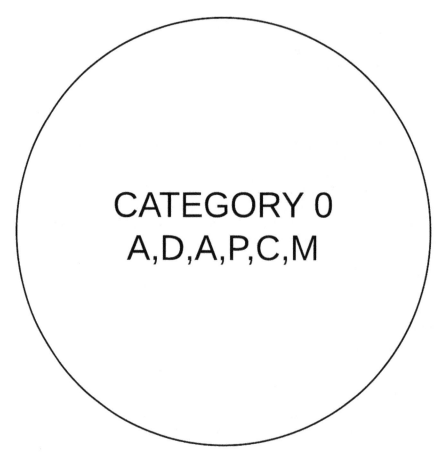

Figure 4.2 Category 0

Category *zero* game developer scale

Category 0 entity (inner collaboration)

We begin with Category 0 which describes a single person, an individual, who is able to do the work of all the disciplines as a one person 'game developer'. All the decisions and collaboration that occur in the making of a game by a category 0 developer, occurs inside their own head, and all the execution, from design to implementation to marketing and release, is done by that one person too. We used to see a lot of this in the earliest days of home computer / game development, for example on the ZX Spectrum with Matthew Smith's Manic Miner & Jet Set Willy and thankfully still do today in the form of App developers releasing entertainment software into the mobile ecosystems of iOS and Google Play stores, though certainly not as common among console or PC game developers.

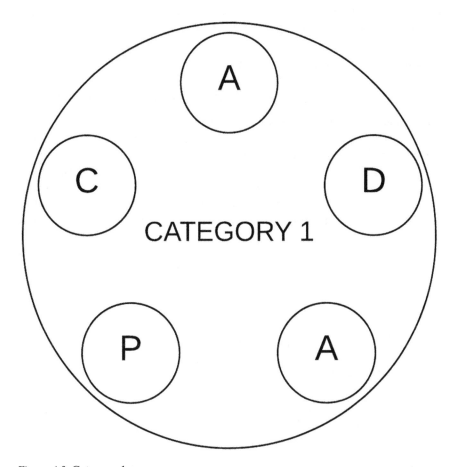

Figure 4.3 Category 1

Category *one* game developer scale

Category 1 entity (horizontal communication between nodes)

As we move up to Category 1, we now have a single person responsible for each discipline. So, one person is fully responsible for the Art, one for Audio, one for Design and so on. Down at this scale, what often tends to happen is that some of those individuals will get to wear different disciplinary 'hats' at different times during production of the game, or one person may even occupy two of the disciplinary spots (for example an audio role, and a producer role, which is a single job that I myself held for two years at a small independent developer). This entity scale is basically one person at each discipline. Communication between these disciplines occurs horizontally, as there is a fairly flat level from discipline to discipline, and, unless development is distributed[2] usually this kind of collaboration can occur in the same office space, as a small developer of this nature can have all personnel be present in a single room if needed.

Category *two* game developer scale

Category 2 entity (horizontal and vertical communication between nodes)

The Category 2 entity now assumes that each discipline is made up of a team. So, we have an audio team, art team and a design team etc. The amount of information flowing between these disciplines now has to operate at not just a horizontal level, like it did with the Category 1 entity, but it also needs to be happening across the multiple vertical levels, for example the directors of each discipline need to be communicating at their horizontal level with other directors, but also up and down their own disciplinary team. At the same

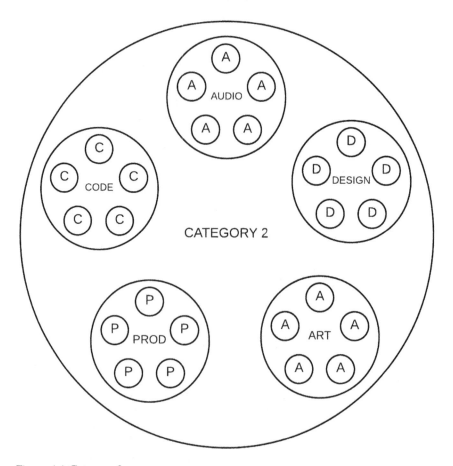

Figure 4.4 Category 2

time, the *leads* in each discipline need to communicate across at their horizontal level with the other leads, as well as up and down in their own disciplines, and the designers and artists also need to communicate horizontally among themselves, as well as up and down in their own disciplinary columns.

Category *three* game developer scale

Category 3 entity (horizontal, vertical and diagonal communication between nodes)

The Category 3 entity is where things start to get big, as this is a *group* of Category 2 entities that are all working on the same game. So we have multiple category 1 teams, all working collaboratively on the same title. This may have many forms, as some of those studios could be specifically working on

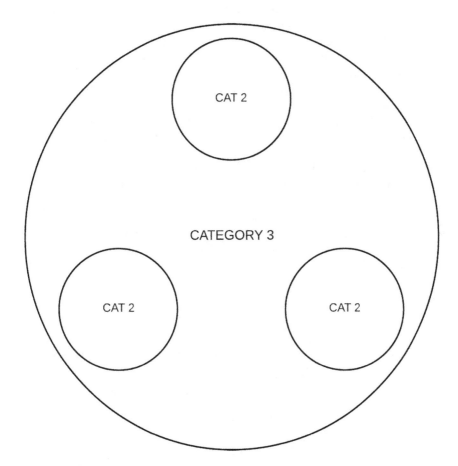

Figure 4.5 Category 3

multiplayer, or single player parts of the game, while in other Category 3 entities, the team may be broken down to work on individual maps across different studios. In every instance, the communication needed is now not just horizontal and vertical but also diagonal across multiple studios with other teams in the same discipline. A lot of this kind of communication and information, though needing to flow freely, in terms of direction and vision (both technical and creative) must also follow quite strict directorial flows. What you cannot have here, are artistic and technical decisions being made at every node, but instead they need to be made and communicated 'to' those nodes from the project direction layer. This is why both technical and creative direction nodes are necessary in such large organisations.

Category 4 and beyond...

Using the game development model to view scale and nodes, I believe that a Category 4 entity is potentially something that is possible, though perhaps only theoretically. It would be made up of two or more Category 3 entities, which would be the equivalent of massive publisher owned multi-studio projects, but that are collaborating on a *single game* across those multiple publishers. While this conceptually seems possible, the reality of two or more publishers working and collaborating at this scale in the real economic world does not yet seem to be a possibility. But, one of the things I particularly loved about the Pacific Rim movies was that they periodically seemed to announce a bigger Kaiju category every time the stakes needing upping, and game development is not exempt from this kind of spectacle.

   With this framework in place, we now have a good model which enables us to look more precisely (though this is still a broad tool) at a developer's organisational priorities and scale, as well as the kinds of communication effort required, and understand the kinds of teams that operate inside these structures. We can also look at and examine a more detailed way of describing game audio is inside a developer... which conveniently leads us into the next chapter – *What is Game Audio?*

Notes

1 An important distinction when it comes to the 'disciplines' across some developers is worth noting. There do exist the notions of cross-discipline teams and employees who migrate between, or oscillate between, different 'traditional' disciplines in order to make games. Cross-discipline development environments allow their workforce to naturally span the disciplines required to create the game. About the best example of this kind of environment is Valve Software. Though they do have the concept of traditional roles within their company, they would consider these more broadly as umbrella categories and not get into the minute niche job description and hierarchies that we might see existing at somewhere like Electronic Arts (Audio Designer III etc.). These kind of cross discipline enrolments tell us a lot about the kinds of games and the kind of development processes that are important to those teams. Agility and fast migration to where the person can be most helpful suggests

a fluid and iterative environment where experimentation and innovation lead and are 'the most important thing'. Whereas very specific jobs titles, with limited encouragement or incentive to think outside those roles, speaks to a more for-mulaic, year on year, development environment where innovation perhaps occurs only at marketing level, rather than at the level of the game design itself. This is not to criticise or hold aloft one model over another, but merely to illustrate the vastly different kinds of entertainment being produced.

2 Distributed development is a development model where members of the team are in different places, sometimes even different countries and time zones, making use of cloud-based documentation, communication and remote access to computers and game builds. This model, and hybrids thereof, is being used more frequently as things like global pandemics become integrated features of game development cul-ture. These features also create *opportunities* for developers to hire people who would not ordinarily be able to make it to the office, because of accessibility issues for example.

5 What is game audio?

The question would seem easy to answer, but once we attempt to answer, we find almost always that the subject confounds us. You may meet someone at a cocktail party who asks what it is you do, and as you attempt to explain your role in game audio, you will find yourself trying to explain this work in terms of other job types and metaphors that the person might be more familiar with. Making audio, or sound, or music, whatever you want to call it, for games is a simple way of answering but as soon as you need to begin delving into more *detail* about what it is that you do then you are going to start to describe a whole array of different areas in which you often and tangentially operate. Even the simple starting point of *making sound effects*, often requires lots of further explanation of the several stages of recording and editing as well as sourcing pre-recorded sounds in sound libraries and mixing them together into new sounds that match the context in which they need to be played. This doesn't even begin to cover the process of getting those sounds to play and be dynamically modified along with the context inside a game engine. I don't think there is an easy, simple way to explain what game audio is, though there are many ways to look at the subject. So, we will be kept in detailed conversations at cocktail parties for a while yet. Though, there are a couple of *usefully descriptive* ways in which to look at explaining and understanding what it is we do.

Game audio: the multi-disciplinary craft

One helpful and illustrative way, and I have hinted at this already, is to think about game audio as being a vast multi-disciplinary area where 'what' we do changes on a weekly, if not daily basis throughout the course of the development of a title. By thinking about audio as deeply cross disciplinary, and generalist, rather than a specialist narrow skillset, we can start to draw a realistic snapshot of some of the areas encompassed inside game audio.

For me, there are three large disciplinary areas that game audio of any kind feeds on, all of which overlap.

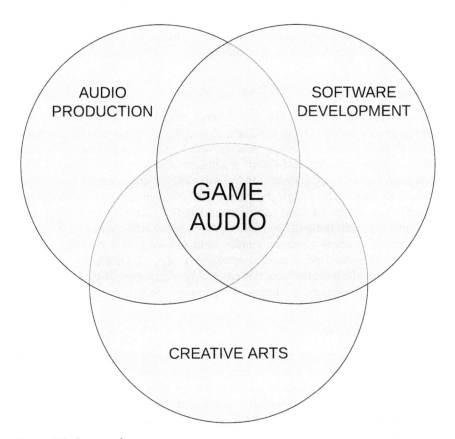

Figure 5.1 Game audio

Audio production

The first broad area of audio production covers a whole slew of skillsets and sub-disciplinary areas within it. Sound recording and music production may be said to be at the heart of this category, with the slew of music recording pro- grammes and music technology courses emerging in the 1990s of which many game audio practitioners came from this background. These courses focussed almost exclusively on the technical skills required of audio engineering, as a way to have vocational-focussed students entering the world of professional audio engineering. Microphone placement and selection skills, multi-tracking, tape splicing and editorial, as well as some significant focus on emerging com- puter-based recording and editing systems like Cubase were certainly a focus on courses of this period. These courses have now modernised, adapted and updated themselves to include all manner of digital sound production work- flows as well as acoustics, sound synthesis and sound mixing, with many also focussing on interactive contexts for sound. The focus on engineering and technical execution provides a good foundation upon which to build creative skills, and also gives confidence in a person's ability to execute and produce something – to take an idea, and to turn it into something tangible.

Creative and narrative arts

The creative and narrative arts are another very broad area of study and experience in which to become immersed, and form fundamentally the *storytelling* element of the medium of video games. A good background to this area will likely include literary and theatre studies, creative writing, filmmaking, also perhaps including graphic design and photography (both powerful storytelling media with deep seams of history, culture and criticism in which to familiarise oneself). The history of film, television and radio is also a vast subject area incredibly rich with potential to feed into the work done in audio within game development, as nearly all games employ some kind of reference to film, or piggyback on these well-established storytelling devices. A familiarity with, and enthusiasm for the narrative arts, will form a significant part of the creative and presentational conversations when working in game audio.

Software development

This undeniably essential element of working in game audio is the ability to work with software, and not with film or another linear medium. The interactive run-time environment of software, brings with it a certain amount of specific development language and indeed culture, though that is changing. It is a given that video games are not a pure form of software development in which only programmers work, it is a multidisciplinary environment with a variety of expertise in each area – however, one of the common elements around which everyone must revolve is that a video game is run-time software, and as such, software development practice is generally at the heart of how games are scheduled, produced and shipped. Software development practices like 'Scrum' are common inside game developers, in addition to the major milestones within every game development team such as Alpha and Beta phases and Vertical and Horizontal Slices. At a very high level, working in software development is close enough to the production phases found within the motion picture or television industries, which typically have three broad areas of pre-production, production (location or on stage shooting) and post-production – this latter phase being typically where the creative audio work tended to be relegated. After all, the distinguishing features between an iterative, multi-disciplinary software development environment, and a film production environment, are the core differences which now allow audio to be a proactive leader within the early prototyping and concept phases of video games development. All this to say that software development practices are still very much at the centre of how we put games onscreen, and the tools with which we are building and executing our creative visions are constantly evolving at an incredibly fast pace. Familiarity with both the history, and current practices within software development, are essential broad areas to be cognizant of in game audio.

Where all three of these broad areas overlap, at the intersection of these three groups of knowledge and experience, can feasibly be described as 'game audio' and the many skillsets and understanding required to operate in that area, necessitate a significant expertise in some, if not all of the areas discussed. As mentioned, this is not a particularly simple way of describing what it is that we do in game audio, so there is a second, much higher-level model which relates directly to the blending and balance of skills that someone working in game audio would ideally need to have.

Game audio: the 33% generalist

In a Designing Sound blog interview in 2011, the film sound designer, Randy Thom, when asked what it was that he spends a typical day doing, came up with this insightful answer:

> I sometimes think of the work as being about 33% art, 33% craft, and 33% human relations. I'm always disappointed when I see 95% of the energy in discussions about sound design being devoted to the craft part. It's the easiest aspect to talk about, and the easiest to accomplish. The art and the human relations are hard to nail down conceptually, and difficult as hell to master in the day to day work. I see so many people who are ProTools wizards but don't have a clue how to relate to clients and collaborators, and who seem lost when trying to make artistic decisions.
>
> (Isaza 2011)

When I first read this, I was immediately struck by the simplicity and beauty of what this described, and the fact that it subverted many of the expectations that people had of those working in audio for film or games, who immediately gravitate to thinking about sound work as technical. Perhaps it was because I have been working in games for such a long time, and working with complex and ever changing problems at the lowest, very detail-driven levels on specific projects, trying to solve and worry about those smallest of problems that are occurring constantly and unpredictably, that I was never able to take enough of a step far enough back to see this much bigger picture that Randy was describing so eloquently. Now, while Randy is of course referring to working in film sound, this balance of types of work describes *extremely* well, the reality of working in video games. A *typical* day – week – or development phase may not strictly exist, or even be describable in reality, but, I would very deliberately choose to describe the work of game audio in this same way, the same mix and balance, of these different areas. This 33% model, when visualised, looks like this…

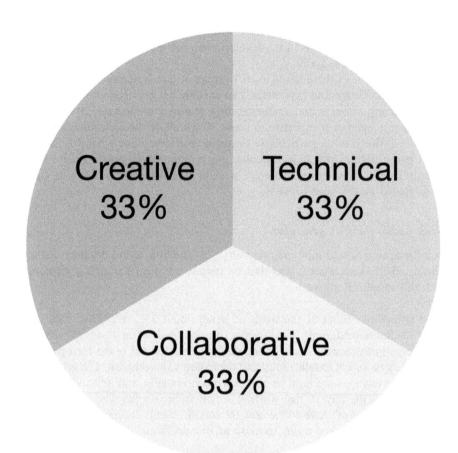

Figure 5.2 The 33% model

One can easily start to apply this directly to game development and game audio very specifically. One could even argue that perhaps video games are perceived even more as a 'technical' medium than film, in that, as we have acknowledged, they are forged in the fires of software development, are continually evolving during production and the act of adding sound to a game is certainly technically and practically more challenging. However, what Randy describes here is the importance of NOT having one of these areas dominate what it is we do inside the craft overall. If we allow technology, and technical skills, to be the defining element of what it is we do, then the creative and aesthetic challenges will always be compromised and judged only by how successful the technical solutions were. This is not how we should be evaluating our success in game audio, or in game development in general. Likewise, we cannot neglect that same technical side in favour of the creative – we cannot run with ideas that 'may' work – we must ultimately be able to execute them in a way that is coherent and clear for the audience. And, of course, perhaps the most neglected part of the whole balancing act (though of course no part is more important than another) is that of *collaboration*. Human interaction with our fellow team members with whom we are building the game *together*. There absolutely must be a solidarity between departments, when it comes to video games, if one discipline fails, *we all fail*. This is the part that I have seen the most underestimated and underdeveloped in sound designer's skillsets – who are mostly (in my experience) comfortable working in silos and measure the success of each project on the success of its audio alone. I have also encountered sound designers who are possessed of an almost super-natural human relation 'aura' with which they are able to communicate in a fun, open and playful way, while still maintaining the professionalism needed to work on a collaborative project with a team. The 'human relations' part is, for many of us, and was admittedly for me, extremely challenging to develop, and an area in which personally I had to do a lot of growing.

To frame this with some personal perspective, my first experience of working with clients was in my first job after graduating from my master's degree at Bournemouth University, when I worked at 'Matinee Sound and Vision', a small boutique sound service studio based in Reading, UK. My role was as a recording engineer, and sometime sound designer and composer. Initially I was very bad at talking with clients, helping them and making sure they felt relaxed, creatively involved and included in the sound work, and also giving a sense of confidence in the work of myself and the company I represented. This is because I was nervous around them. Luckily, I received some rapid, to-the-point feedback after a few client recording sessions, and thankfully, because I had very good managers who were able to quickly get this feedback to me in a way that *motivated* me, along with suggestions of things to try, I was able to correct the behaviours, spent more time learning the pipeline in the studio to increase my confidence and *focus* on the client – making sure I looked after them, involved them in the creative process and exceeded their expectations. Seeing this area of Randy's quote so prominently in the mix of the day to day work of sound motivated me even further to change habits that, later in my professional in-house audio developer career, I had developed. I had mistakenly believed that when I found my way into full-time employment *inside* a game development studio, that I no longer had the pressure and daily stress of working with 'clients' to deal with, and for me, I would overly cocoon myself inside an isolated studio, working quietly on my own for long periods of time. The motivation provided in Randy's quote was precisely what I needed to grow, and to get out of this rut I had created for myself. A lot of other things started to come together at this time for me too, including facing a lot of the anxieties that I had about public speaking and standing up in front of the team to give audio updates. By facing these head-on, I was able to grow significantly in confidence and move into more directorial and leadership roles. I managed this by volunteering for as many public speaking engagements as I could, and the first time I had even attended the Game Developer's Conference

(GDC) in San Francisco was also the first time I had spoken in public – giving a one hour talk on the mixing work my team had done on the game. This was obviously terrifying, and a huge risk, but I got through it, with a lot of rehearsal, and once it was over, realised that I *really* enjoyed it.

All this to say, that the realisation that working successfully and sustainably in game audio required equal balance and an equal attention to these three important areas of the work was a complete revelation for me. Game audio was something that I had always thought was technically demanding and required *mastery* of that technology, but also one which was creatively driven, meaning my ideas about the sounds were, for me, the more important factor. Understanding the missing collaborative element helped put everything into a balanced and attainable approach. It also provided me with a way to very quickly describe what it was that I did as a game audio developer to deeply experienced professionals in sound, others in parallel disciplines and also to

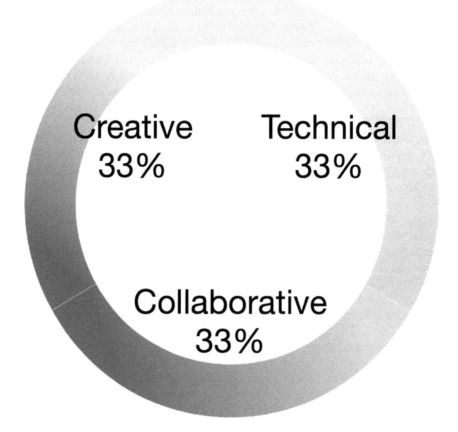

Figure 5.3 The 33% model with blend

people outside of the industry entirely. It also allowed me to explain very quickly the kinds of skills that were necessary to be successful in game audio to people wishing to get into, or further grow their confidence and abilities as well as showcasing a high-level vision that could be applied to practically any project or development team that I happened to be working at. As a leader of a sound team, it also provided a system through which to identify ways the team members could grow, by striving for balance among those three areas and by training and encouraging more exploration in the underdeveloped areas. What I love about the 33% image is its simplicity, although when I was visualising it, I realised that you couldn't really draw solid and distinct lines between creative, collaborative or technical skills. In many ways, a lot of the work of an audio designer would bleed from one area to another, with perhaps one task consisting of all three of the areas required in quick succession to get something playing onscreen in the build. So a more interesting way, though slightly less visually appealing and beautifully simple, is a 'gradient bleed' version of that same image where each of the three areas *blends* into the next... (see figure 5.3).

So, with these two overall explorations and definitions of what game audio actually is: the first being the multi-disciplinary skill sets in which video game sound and production work evolved into the heavily multi-skilled and hybrid role that it is, and the second, the high-level view of balanced game development work, in terms of technical, creative and collaborative modes of the day-to-day work itself as idealistic goal, we now have a reasonably firm grip (which is about as much as you can hope for) on what game audio *really* is – and armed with these fundamental lenses on the craft, we can further reflect on how audio can really lead the process of game development, rather than following in the turbulent wake of the ship.

6 What you may be missing

Vision to drive your tools and pipelines

> Experimenters delight in how fast they take a concept from words to sketch, to model, and, yes, to a successful new offering.
>
> (Kelley 2005)

Technology must follow

In many game development team structures, the games that are made are still firmly classed in the technology category. Indeed, many people will assume that video games are unequivocally *software* and are developed and consumed as such. However, while video games are certainly, by definition, software (and they have been developed and built mostly using software development practices), more recently, video games are being understood by both audiences and by those making and marketing them as 'entertainment' rather than software. Actually, I suspect games have always been *marketed* as entertainment, so I think the more profound shift is on the way games are made, not marketed. The mercurial definition of video games can be challenging to anyone trying to understand the complete picture of this industry. There is now a greater urgency and necessity emerging to conceive video games as entertainment driven by ideas, stories and aesthetics, rather than by and as technologies. Technology is increasingly becoming the invisible means by which ideas are delivered to the player, and the means by which the game developers are able to articulate and express their ideas on screen is also echoed in the dramatic changes in tools focussed on *creator-experience*. Leading with ideas and driving projects with a creative vision is now more deeply embedded in the culture at many successful, and ambitious, developers and publishers. Sound certainly can quickly re-align with this shift in development priorities, in fact, this shift represents an enormous opportunity in which audio can be a leading star of establishing and expressing those creative ideas leading game conception and development. Using such an entertainment-driven approach, rather than having audio that is driven by the tools and workflows available, we need to shape, influence and define the creative ideas and requirements of what will be the project's 'audio vision'. Our audio tools can be shaped and twisted to deliver the artistic vision. These tools have to be flexible enough to support and bend to the weight of new ideas, be designed around satisfying a creative user experience and are being made in order that the process of making something with these tools is both satisfying and feels every bit like crafting and articulating an *idea* as you work with, structure and shape the sonic material directly. The need now is very much on developing vision that drives your technology – and this is a trend that will continue to run deeper as tools become easier to use, easier to access in terms of cost and as old processor and memory limitations and red-lines evaporate. Invisibility is the watchword of this movement – as we move away from the physically present workhorse of personal computing into streamed and distributed cloud based development environments via cloud computing; simultaneously, the more the technology we work with becomes invisible and frictionless, the more our tools themselves are becoming focussed on enabling us to dream and play to invent.

Low friction tools

In order to more freely explore ideas and creative impulses, the tools we are using need to become virtually invisible to the designer, becoming as low friction as possible. That is to say that the idea is always the driver, and the means to express those ideas onscreen, in as quick and painless a way possible, is a priority. All pipelines ideally need to foreground this frictionless approach to the creator. That is to say that once the idea can be expressed in the tools, the content and implementation from sound source to audio engine and to game engine should be, where possible, the fewest steps possible, as simple and intuitive as possible and as *accessible* as possible. We are looking for a zero-frustration creator environment. The Integration and playback of audio design should never be where the designer spends the majority of their time, struggling to perform basic sound playback and expressing and trying out basic playback logic like randomisation or prioritisation. Visual scripting in many toolsets is similarly becoming increasingly intuitive and simplified, leaning deep into the graphic visualisation and smooth, responsive UX increasingly focussed on run-time experimentation and fluidity. There should be as few layers of abstraction as possible, meaning that audio designers, while some may be able to write script or code themselves, should never be thinking about sound in terms of code, but should be conceiving of their work as *sound ideas* that the player will experience. The player will have zero exposure to the tools or pipelines you are using and won't care how much you fought against the technology to get something basic to work. They *will care* if the resulting experience isn't very good and brings them out of the engagement in the world. I would push much further the idea of tools being frictionless to the creators and say that tools need to go beyond frictionless and be *fun and pleasurable* to use – this is so that creative values of playfulness and fun can be integral parts of a real-time sound implementation and manipulation system, and in order to stimulate and enable creative thinking away from the production sound asset level, and more towards the run-time experience level.

While I understand that this is a high-level ambition of tools and pipelines used in the creation of sound and music at run-time, the method of working creatively in sound, for me, is inspired by the way I work on a day to day basis, removing almost all interactive dependencies, at the idea level, and working directly with sound and image.

Beginnings

All creative exploratory work for me tends to begin with adding sounds to images. My process usually starts long before there is any game engine to work with, because we are developing a very high level idea together with the team just verbally or on paper. This ideation is something that has to happen long before we get near the game engine – because at this level, removed from technical restrictions of any kind, we can deal with the fundamentally creative, very basic elements of the idea, regardless of whether it is a game or not. We need to be certain that the idea for the game, the world, the story, is first an engaging one, an exciting one, that causes whoever experiences it to desire more – in order to do this there needs to be not only clarity to the vision, but perhaps equally a good measure of ambiguity. It is good if there are questions and it is great if the people seeing and hearing idea want to know more. This phase of work is always easiest for me in the DAW (Digital Audio Workstation) with which I am the most familiar. These days that is either Nuendo, or Reaper depending really on nothing more than a mood preference and *feel* for the different user interfaces than anything else.

Tone development

The creative process often starts with trying to assemble some kind of tonal or spatial emotion to go with either a still concept image, or a concept video. The process involves looking at the material, reacting to it and trying out various sounds to find something that resonates in an interesting way with the image, perhaps the emotion of being there in that place (it is very often a location in a world that a *character* finds themselves in that concerns most concept images at the beginning of projects). The resonance may not be correct, or what we want, but every resonance tells us something. It also involves imagining what the point-of-view of a character is in that place, what their attitude and personality is, their relationship to the scale of the world they are in, these are some of the entry points that we can try to get across in the sound that is being imagined. Sometimes I don't have any visual material to work with, and this makes things more challenging, but not impossible. It is always possible to work like this with 'borrowed' imagery; a mysterious image taken from the Amazon jungle (or any jungle or forest for that matter) capturing some of the dramatic light or scale of the environment; it could be anything that fits the *idea* and the environment visually and enables you to start throwing sounds at that imagery and seeing what happens, in terms of layering in the sound perspective.

Once we are 'in' the image (the process of getting your head and heart inside the world that is proposed by the visual), whatever it is, and some ideas and moods begin to present themselves, it is then a matter of sifting and editing through the sound material and adding and removing it. Previewing, editing, playing, iterating, previewing the work in progress to colleagues to get reactions, and eventually removing all the things that don't fit. This process could begin with sound, with ambience, with textures, or it could begin with music, perhaps just a subtle texture. You may begin to build a maximalist approach to support a maximalist image or contrast a busy image with a minimalist sound – any variety of approaches may be entertained and tested, ideas will form, be tested and perhaps evaporate. The material you use can come from anywhere at this stage, and by the end of the process, you could have three or four different 'directions' that can be presented and discussed with the team or one on one with the creative director and other trusted colleagues. The things that really resonate can then be amplified or highlighted in your next version. The process continues until the visuals and sounds start to feel fixed, and at this point we are usually able to start previewing for the wider team in tandem with some description and explanation, all the while fine-tuning and re-adjusting the work as a whole.

Fast, fluid tools

The process I describe here is reliant on my tools (Nuendo and Reaper) and me being familiar enough with them and how they work to be able to very quickly add and remove and process sound material on a timeline. The process of me learning to use those tools was a fairly quick one, in which the majority of the learning occurred within the first few days or weeks of being hands-on with them. Very gradually and sporadically I will encounter and learn new features in the software, and sometimes these will influence my overall workflows in positive ways, like being able to create template sessions for particular tasks like sound design, dialogue editing, or trailer work. I am certainly not concerned with mastery of the software *before* I can consider myself 'qualified' to be able to use them to creative ends. If I am evaluating new tools, and quickly hit a roadblock in usability, I will almost always never return to that software again. My thinking here is that because I need to get work done and executed continually, the software will need to be creatively rewarding and playful for me to abandon the methods I have already established and can use quickly and easily. Generally, if I'm investigating a new tool I really need to have a good amount of time to make mistakes and learn the new work patterns, and if you are *shipping* a game it is not an ideal time to do this. Concept and pre-production do offer opportunities to expand your toolsets because you have an expanded sense of time, and different kinds of pressures. However, because the concept phase is so fast moving, and there is a lot of sound work being done, this is also now becoming a time where every second becomes precious to a sound designer, lead or director, and having to learn new tools and try out new methods of working can hinder or frustrate the creative flows required in that period too. But by building and scheduling time for R&D that includes this investigative process, the pressure to instantly succeed can be eased. It used to be that at the beginnings of projects the sound department typically had very little to do that was *creatively* expansive, so sound teams would revert to sharpening their *technical* solutions, and spend lots of time getting proprietary technical solutions in place. To some extent, we now have widely available third-party tools that are enriched enough to be able to replace the kind of frantic technology building that used to occur for the majority of concept and pre-production.

Pipelines

Understanding the difference between 'tools' and 'pipelines' is extremely important, especially when requesting or looking at where improvements can be made in a game development process. As a project moves into production focussed work, with deliveries and deadlines, we inevitably look more towards defining both the role of tools, and their place in a pipeline.

The easiest way to think about the difference is that a tool is a single node within a pipeline, and that tool will have ins and outs from and to other tools or processes. All these nodes, inputs and outputs, considered together in a chain, or 'flow' make up the pipeline which is used to generate a 'build',[1] a working piece of software that compiles, runs and is playable and tuneable. The build is continually being regenerated and iterated upon, and more often than not, the build itself becomes a part of the pipeline that is necessary in order to preview changes and tweaks to be made to the sound at what is often referred to as 'run-time'.

Note

1 The build, or game build, is basically a continually updated version of the final compiled (or cooked) version of the game. Usually it is updated every hour or so, by incorporating new changes and additions or revisions in the code or content. This is then played and reviewed in order to ascertain what changes need to be made to subsequent builds.

7 Communication essentials

Managing expectations of quality
(the 'L' scale)

When it comes to execution and production realities, an extremely important part of working in audio with other disciplines on a project is being able to thoroughly *manage expectations* and communicate the trajectory of the expected quality of the audio at any given moment. This is not something that is easy to do, and I have found a good method which is simple and straightforward enough for all disciplines inside and outside of audio to understand – whether you are working on prototyping, polishing features, cinematics, music or voice, this will help.

For every component or feature, and every *milestone* that a feature goes through, I apply and communicate a simple 'L value' to the audio. Simply meaning 'quality level', this is a measure of where I expect the audio quality to be for that particular element at a particular review milestone. It helps not only the producers and other directors of the project to know what the level of quality they expect to hear is, but it also helps the audio designers working on that element to know what level of expected quality it is they need to be concerned with for each milestone. Typically, I use a 4-level approach and it is roughly defined as follows... (see figure 7.1)

As can be seen in figure 7.1, if we are working in early prototyping along with the rest of the team, the sound at Level 1 is something that can be provided and worked on to only give feedback and make sure the correct timing is happening with very rough placeholder sound, music or voice assets. This is the foundational element of providing sound extremely early; the benefits of this are huge, as the integration and thinking of sound playback and triggering at these early stages can highlight many potential problems with a feature, as well as discovering opportunities for sound within the *design* of any feature. Sound is extremely loosely defined here at L1 and doesn't necessarily even need to fit the aesthetic direction of the audio, so can be stubbed in quickly. As long as you have communicated the L table to the team in advance, and have it conveniently available to refer to (a link to a shard confluence page or similar), and communicated in any meetings that the sound will *only be taken to L1*, then everyone can be freed to focus on prototyping and experimenting with the feature without the need to worry about authoring sounds that are final and polished – another term for this is Low Fidelity Prototyping a concept taken from UX design

AUDIO CONDITIONS OF SATISFACTION

CoS Level	Audio Expectations	Iteration & Collaboration	Throwaway Sound?	Description	Dialogue Example	SFX example	Music Example	Mix
L1	BASIC FEEDBACK: Anything requiring TIMING, PACING, CADENCE, FEEDBACK validation. Audio should be in the loop, i.e. provide the rough sounds, but does not (necessarily) need to be the one integrating the sounds.	Low to Mid	100%	*Low Fidelity Prototype. Audio is integrated in first pass, feedback and timing format only = rough, dirty, proves functionality and provides timing feedback for player that can be used to validate the feature – does not need to follow style-guide principles.*	*Robot voice triggered lines provide structure and rough timing.*	*Footsteps have one or two variations, and are triggered so we can hear the tempo of walk run cycles etc*	*If needed, a single piece of music provides an overall sense of the tempo and emotion.*	*Extremely rough, rudimentary mix*
L2	IDENTITY: Audio generally remains loose and pliable so we can be agile and tweak the feature, but feels like the game (identity is present). Feature recipes may be locked after this stage.	Mid to High	80%	*Audio is integrated in second pass format = More polished in terms of balance, mix and variations for a more enjoyable player experience. Timing and cadence is tightened. Assets are not yet considered final from a creative standpoint, but should be using project style-guide recipes for aesthetics.*	*This would be temp, but real human voice actors from either the studio or local temp actors.*	*Footsteps match the real character and have the right amount of variations and the right, tuned tempo and rough mix to match the emotion and transitions.*	*If needed, several music tracks provide rough dynamics of the system and support those emotional changes.*	*A 'priority' mix is applied to all elements ('what is the most important thing' should be answered.)*
L3	POLISH: At end of this phase, expect to work with final animation and VFX assets. Director punchlist driven.	High	50%	*Audio is fully integrated and 'shippable quality'. The audio features like SFX and VO feature final recorded assets, the correct amount of variations per sound trigger, is well pre-mixed and timing and feedback to the player is perfected.*	*A professional actor is used for the actual timing and emotion of the line(s)*	*Full variations, surface detection, pre-mixed and timing is locked. A full dynamic system accounting for all speeds and types of interactivity.*	*Music is composed specifically for the feature and transitions are integrated between system dynamics.*	*Pre-mixes are done per food-group (sfx, vo, mus) - overall loudness targets and panning rules are satisfactorily met.*
L4	FINAL AUDIO PASS: Game is locked, rest of team is ideally locked out of submit process.	Very Low	5%	*Audio receives final polish pass (this is a standalone audio phase at the end).*	*Final mix of all approved recordings.*	*Final mix of all SFX elements*	*Final orchestral or instrumental recordings are integrated and mixed*	*Final mix (shippable). Meets loudness targets.*

Figure 7.1 Conditions of satisfaction levels

principles, and the advantages of low fidelity prototyping are 100% applicable here in concept phase of sound (inexpensive, fast, collaborative, illuminating, iterative, easy to get feedback and quickly pivot to tackle issues).

For the L2 pass, this is the moment when a feature is now solid enough to be able to support slightly more polished sound work in line with the vision of the aesthetics This could also be thought of as a mid-fidelity prototype – meaningful feedback and testability with players, easy buy in from clients and stakeholders – though costs, time and team sizes will often need to be higher to achieve this. It is also a chance to start to get some of the *feeling* and identity into the sounds of the feature itself – assets may now have more emotional impact and be more tailored to fit the triggers and sync of the feature. Again, communicating that the L2 pass is expected, helps everyone to understand that you are now also working on the sonic 'identity' and feeling of the feature.

For the L3 pass, this is where a great deal of integration and iteration will occur to *really* polish the feature, there will be many play-tests and a lot of feedback gathered from as many sources as possible in order to get the feature as tight as possible, many sound assets may now be entering what feels like an *almost* final state, although the feature will still be undergoing some major iteration and scoping as it approaches its final phase and other disciplines add polish like visual effects that also affect the sound. This is most certainly the *high-fidelity prototype* stage – indeed it isn't really fair to call features in the game prototypes at this point, (perhaps 'benchmarks' is better), but the analogy still holds up as we remain in an iterative and collaborative mode of creation, in which many factors are still changing and moving all around us; it is also the stage whereby problems become much harder and more difficult to resolve, sometimes involving complex rework resulting in some major bugs and also in regressions where one discipline's check-in will break the functionality of another discipline's work. If there is any final content being created towards the end of this phase, it is more likely that final recorded content will need to be redone, actors recalled, composers and musicians recalled to re-author cues, etc. – so many of the truly 'final' elements for audio are deferred until...

L4! For an L4 audio pass to happen, everything needs to be in an approved and locked state on the part of the feature itself, that is animation, visual effects, all the tuning and balancing, This enables audio to make the final sound sync polishing pass, and any final mix adjustments, and the final round of punch-list driven reviews which are focussed to the appropriate level of detail expected in L4. You should never really be pushing anything to an L4 state unless you are fully benchmarking the final quality of something, as might be done in an extremely polished vertical slice milestone. L4 represents the final moments of a feature's design lifespan, in which the finished component receives the final recorded assets, and most importantly the final mixing and balancing of *all* the sound elements, not just of the feature, but of all the other areas around that feature.

Without the ability to express to a team which quality level of sound you are working on, the expectations of the team will always be open to interpretation, some of them will expect to have the final audio feel in the early prototypes, and while this is something that can of course be done by an audio team, by either going all out in terms of sound design, or using finished assets from existing games or movies (particularly in the case of music) but use of existing assets sets a dangerous precedent, and false expectations of the following phases, while also somewhat creatively painting your team into a corner. It is also vitally important for your audio team to realise that they are not expected to focus on the identity of the sound in L1, this frees them up to fully support and be a part of the fast iteration and throwaway mentality that is necessary for a successful prototype and incubation stage. The key is to remain in the sketch mentality early on and polish only later.

So, for every element of the sound you are working on, it is vitally important to know, and then communicate outwards to everyone else involved, the quality levels of sound that are needed at that particular time.

When working early on with a team in audio, it is really vital to communicate this very different design *mentality* that is required at each of these levels, whether it is that of a throwaway mindset, where the audio designers should assume that 99.9% of their work is throwaway –therefore not to waste time and energy making it sound amazing and polishing it, when it will get thrown out, or cut, or refined beyond the original remit several times a week. Taking away the emphasis on the need to produce final quality work and understanding this long-term path to arrive at that final quality work, is certainly one of the most important elements of leading a team with sound.

8 Audio in concept

Of course, in the extremely early phases of production like pre-concept and concept, there very well may be no 'feature' on which to work, and no game engine up and running in which to try things out. At this stage, we are *not* operating within the scope of the L scale at all because *execution* is not a concern – instead we are in a pre-implementation phase of creative exploration and ideation. This is an early stage for sound that I have found very rarely documented at all, so we will continue to dig into this topic a little more here with regards to getting involved in that ideation process early in useful ways with sound. For the embryonic, pre-implementation phase of any project, there are numerous ways in which audio can play a leading role.

The importance of high-level vision and direction

A great many audio directors start out in their roles after being promoted from sound lead or senior sound implementer. As such they are raised in an environment which places great importance and emphasis on low-level details, mid-level forecasting (threat detection) and systemic designs. Dealing with high level intangibles can be new and daunting for this risk-averse mindset. A high-level audio vision necessitates exploration before establishing rules and designs that are *not* derived from technological or implementational limitations, ideally, the high-level audio vision will completely disregard any thoughts and considerations of implementation. It often helps to think of these high level rules as being 'franchise' rules, rather than specific to a *game* you are making, meaning you can think about the sound vision at such a high level regardless of whether this is a movie, a TV show or a game – it may end up being all three – the *vision* is rarely defined by the fact you are making a game. Regardless of the medium, the methodology is the same – you are defining what the fundamental rules of this universe are. Often times, those rules are shared by many disciplines, and are put in place by a creative director, or similar high-level creative visionary, who is able to *distill* what is important, and essential, about the franchise being crafted. Being freed from the mid and low-level concerns of a game can be liberating, but also frustrating (throwaway work) and scary (uncertainty). Working without 'proof' that the rules will work in a game, is a leap of faith. But constant work on concepts – applying your rules to various small prototypes like animation benchmark videos or ripomatic trailers – can provide the confidence and reassurance necessary to lock down the high-level rules. There must be enough ambiguity and interpretative stretchiness in your high-level goals that they may be applied in different ways to suit different needs at the lower levels – and challenging and testing your high-level pillars is absolutely necessary. It is also worth noting that even though you may celebrate the success of these rules early on in production, you should not be too afraid to modify them to better fit the evolving moods of the project as time passes on the production. It can take courage to do this, especially if a significant change is needed, but as long as changes are communicated and acknowledged, the better your chance of making something that works for the game, so you don't end up polishing something that is fundamentally broken.

Creative direction: what does it look like and how does it work for audio?

Every single video game project is unique. Not only is the idea for each game unique in the nuance and ways in which it is conceived and implemented, but also the team who is employed to make and bring the game to life is also completely unique and has its own influences, solutions and culture that all weigh and influence the many tributaries of the path to the development of every title. It seems like an obvious truth to say that there is no *one way* to 'make' audio for a game, just in the same way that there is no one way to make that game – the people and their ideas are a critical dimension to the work. Even if you are releasing a similar game on a yearly cadence, the context in which that game is created and the market into which it is released continually changes. The audience and market expectations of what you make at a particular time are completely different every time, and even if it is the exact same team year on year, the team you work with to create and ship the game are different every time, they will grow, change their opinions, modify methods, drink in new influences and have differing concerns – and things change even more as new team members arrive and old ones move on.

So, on day one, or whenever you are together for the first time with your team, and you begin to think about the audio vision on your new project, you will be embarking on a journey that will be completely unique compared to anything you've done before. Everything will have to be figured out from scratch, with new approaches. Even tried-and-tested tools and techniques may be revisited and re-assessed due to post-mortems that have been written after the last game, sometimes in order to make processes more efficient, easier to understand, and sometimes to tweak, to iterate, to adjust or introduce new working methods. Now, you may not need to build or even rebuild your own tools and pipelines, maybe you already have that figured out, but you will need to think about and plan how you will need to deploy those tools and pipelines in order to make your specific game – you will need to apply a high level vision.

Concept phase, for me, has more recently become the area where I appear to be the busiest and most involved in collaborating across disciplines with fluidity – removing barriers wherever I find them, and looking for opportunities to add sound to other's work. It is a time at which I don't feel like an audio designer or director, but more like someone involved in a creative project with a team of collaborators. Basically, it is a time of experimenting and helping to build prototypes – making lots of different pieces, some of which might eventually move forward to become a game. It is where I can start to feel more like a game developer than a mere audio team member – and I think this is because it is *ideas* that we are working with, and not so much sounds or those various production-based categories of a soundtrack. When I start working with sound material, and sketching those early ideas, I am also very much thinking beyond just the audio alone, and using elements like video and text as well as perhaps some very lo-fi interactive elements, like sound play buttons laid out on a PowerPoint presentation page, just to get things triggering onscreen. A lot of my work concerns timing, and cadence, tone and feel.

Developing early audio visions

Here are a few quick and hopefully easy-to-follow examples of how to begin the work of defining a creative vision, very early on, that can be easily communicated to a team. The key with all of these methods, and many more that you will be able to put into action yourself, is that they allow for ideas to be rigorously tested and challenged by playing them for the team, by getting feedback on very early sketch versions of everything that you make. Because you are working so early in the concept phase, you will most likely be grabbing material from other pre-existing games, movies or radio plays, that inspire you about the potential direction that the sound may take. Playing with these raw materials can bring a very polished and finished feel to the work that is being put together and mixed very quickly, so there are distinct advantages to this kind if material being presented to a team (always with the disclaimer that the material is taken from pre-existing media where necessary).

A game director, or creative director is almost always too busy to focus on sound in much depth. In this early phase, and arguably far beyond it, you will essentially need to become the *creative director for audio*. Every moment of your working day will be focussed, in some manner, on the audio vision and resonance with the overall creative vision of the game. Crafting, re-crafting, removing everything that doesn't work, updating, communicating, even if that is in just the 'audio only' version for the very early stages of concept with no visuals at all.

Emotion and feel

Establishing a short piece of storytelling audio that brings the listener into the temporal and aesthetic world of the proposed game is one of the ways of being first into the new world you are exploring. This can be conveyed purely in sound, as in a radio play or drama, or as a trailer style clip or teaser. Similarly, this exploration can be done in conjunction with concept art or dramatic material from other sources. In every instance it is a process of validation with the creative team, after which the piece may be used to communicate back to the team some essence of what is being created. A lot of work can go into this – from writing to editing and sound design as well as music editorial, and investigations into the right *use* of music for the project.

The advance guard

This is the process of material gathering. It is the mindset and approach of running far ahead with ideas and explorations in a particular direction to explore their validity. There is a lot of room at this stage to really go as far and wide as possible with ideas and inspirations – it will quickly become apparent what can be discarded for any given project, but the thing to be mindful of while exploring this methodology is to gather material from as wide a range of sources as possible, then arrange all these elements into various groupings of emotional ideas or various resonances. Some example groupings may be: combat, melancholy, mystery, nostalgia, action and so on. Then, these sounds, once collected and roughly grouped, can be quickly thrown into demos and other visual tests that are being worked on, and just as quickly removed and replaced. The advantage of having a lot of material already gathered and prepared into groups, means that you can work even more quickly with other people right next to you, or sharing a screen live, to be able to get instant reaction as you work together to find tone.

Audio-only concepts

Concept 'imagery' is not just for the visual departments; a concept image can be put together with an audio design which can illicit an entirely different dimension of immersion and effect on an audience. Even if the visual art direction for the game has not yet been defined or fully developed, an audio concept can be made in which the listener can *imagine* any visuals that are conjured in their mind. Sound can be used to open the door to new worlds and new ideas, into which visual images can then flood. This can be especially useful for the art director who will 'see' more of their version of the world as they hear your sounds. The use of sound, music and voice is all acceptable here in an audio concept and can convey action, emotion, space, tone, character – if you model your audio concept on an environment, or a performance, or a piece of music, artists can respond and be inspired to sketch and render things that occur to them from hearing and feeling the emotion in the audio concept.

Working quickly with audio ideas to picture (concept art)

If a piece of concept art does already exist, or if reference images from pre-existing visual material is being gathered, an audio exploration can be applied to these images.

I get to know the concept team, look over their shoulders, talk with them about their remits and what kinds of worlds or characters or elements they are working to conjure through imagery. We quickly discover that what drives their visions are simple adjectives and verbs – and it is these same emotive words that can fuel sonic imagination and work – and by offering to collaborate with them, even if only in an 'on the side' capacity, just to quickly add some sound or music, or even voice, to get the hang of stimulating both the eye and the ear, this work will help to expand the notion of the concepts and begin conversations around the elements of those images that can be taken further in sound, to go where visuals cannot – to render what is not seen in the images.

This kind of work can be achieved for example, by making a video montage of images, audio design can then quickly and easily be applied in your DAW of choice. There is no correct *way into* a piece of concept audio, and one element, like a music cue, or example line of dialogue, could be a key to unlocking the rest of the audio scene, which may then start to build around that anchoring sound. Alternately, slowly building up elements from background to foreground can work equally well, before dropping in a key sound like a dialogue voice-over, music cue or iconic sound element.

The advantage of working to concept images is that you already have the visual dimension to inspire you and bounce ideas off, a sand box to work within, and you can work both inside and outside the frame of that image – adding audio details for what is depicted onscreen in the images, but also thinking about what might be offscreen, outside the frame but also audible to a listener who would be in that location.

Documentation and organization

Everything you do should be as well organized and clearly documented as possible. From keeping your folder structure in project phases like pre-concept, concept, pre-production etc. to organizing music inspiration folders, containing and tracking also rejected examples – those sometimes prove useful when you need something at the last minute that you thought didn't quite work for a particular reason, but suddenly now works perfectly because something in the emotional needs of a particular showcase trailer now requires exactly that. The process of being creatively open to ideas and of jumping from one micro project to the next can be quite a chaotic one, and the availability of a structured way to access your sound sources and designs from those chaotic impromptu sessions is extremely useful later. If you are the kind of person who finds this kind of organization a challenge, this could also be an area of the work that you delegate. Having to explain what sounds are, and what ideas they represent, to another person is also a very useful process to go through in terms of expressing and articulating the work that is being done, usually this kind of sound exploration work happens at an instinctual and non-verbal level for long periods of the day – so articulating it verbally may also help to discover some new dimensions to the work.

Understanding the keywords and phrases that are driving the creative vision

An essential part of building audio vision, and audio direction, is to explore the meaning, in terms of sound, of the key creative phrases that are driving the project. Experimenting and finding out what these key phrases mean for sound is extremely valuable, and if you can already make some elements of sound and approaches to the audio that really resonate with the higher level creative message, then the likelihood of the sounds being created and getting the team excited are much higher. Even taking your project's short 'elevator pitch' and turning that into an audio concept could be an excellent way of getting started. Often you just need that initial framing device which defines what the project is all about, in order to start assembling and editing your audio concept montages.

Validate and challenge

Taking a single, early idea in several different directions – to find where the edges of the idea are and begin to establish some working rules about what works and what doesn't - is essential. Again, a throwaway mentality is vital for all this kind of work, in that each option that is provided should not need to have a lot of time put into it, as the more work is put into a particular direction, the more the effort involved starts to colour one particular option over another. This method also provides opportunities to see what is possible aesthetically and what works, from density (minimal to maximal), and mood, (excitement level) to some notion of the imagined feel and end quality (through use of pre-existing finished and mastered assets).

Once you have moved into concept phase *proper*, out of the nebulous *pre-concept phase*, this is a fantastic opportunity to bring in some colla-borators, like composers, to work with you on some pitches and concept material using the game direction established during pre-concept. This way, original material may now be produced that reacts to the remits of the project itself. This kind of material has a distinct advantage over using pre-existing materials from other films or games – the over-use of temporary assets always paints creative options into a corner, it can take the music or sound into a place it cannot really back out of, there is a real danger of creating something that a team or creative director has fallen in love with. From here, the job of your composer or sound artist is merely to *recreate* what already exists. Beginning this early with *original* material frees everyone from these preconceived ideas and enormously increases the chances of originality and freshness. As this is material that is being used to inspire the rest of the team, in the other disciplines it will also often have the nudging effect to inspire them to work in a more original frame of mind too, perhaps bringing in artists whose work has inspired the team in pre-concept, to actually work together on some original concept art, rather than continuing to copy or imitate a pre-existing aesthetic or feel.

Boiling it all down

The essence of all this work is to boil the ideas down into the easiest to understand concepts and talking points that describe what the sound of the game is all about. If you can boil it all down to one word or a short memorable phrase, or three elements of one word each, then you can easily expand these later through discussion and conversation. The broader your concept, the more readily you can apply the concepts across any aspect of the game, especially once you have it all collapsible down to a single word.

Out of all this creative exploration and aesthetics research, you may need to begin creating and implementing some prototypes or mock ups, essentially some *practical expressions* of the visions of the audio in an interactive environment such as Wwise sound-caster, or even in a freely available, easily accessible game engine context like Unity or Unreal where prototyping is relatively unimpeded by the need for complex networked build pipelines. This testing is a natural next step in the process of demonstrating your direction, to prove some of your sound principles with more concrete examples and applications – by continually testing and challenging your vision and recipes you can see how far they hold up to the oncoming implementation challenges of making an actual game.

All this will help to further define and refine your sound principles, as well as driving your choices and decisions for how and what technology needs to be put in place to serve this vision.

For all of these phases in pre-concept or concept, it is very important to have a completely direct and open collaboration with the creative team, however large or small that may be, though often it is by nature very small. There are cases of comparatively large teams engaging in pre-conception work, though it tends to become something of a production, as it is difficult for a large team to be unstructured and free for a sustained period of time. There may well be a game engine and assets running too, perhaps in tandem to the creative experimentation and exploration. This can be a good moment in which to test ideas onscreen, though, again, the game engine itself will often be a risky place to try out early creative ideas, because of the limitations enforced on the content when implementing an idea. Structure and optimization of assets will start to shape the material, and these will be the elements that provide the *limitations*, rather than the limitations being worked on and figured out on the aesthetic and creative level first.

Though the work you do in this early phase may feel confusing, disorientating and frustrating, it is necessary for sound to be included with the ideation team and figuring things out *together*. In the end, a single two-minute piece of audio can be all that is needed to ignite an idea that can lead to the opening up of avenues of possibilities that had never been considered previously.

Part II

Sound design

Why do we need sounds?

This next section of the book will focus on sound design and will mark the shift of focus into the more specific features of each of the big four food-groups, giving time to dig into each category, and uncover some of the sub-topics within. This will afford us a more complete view of what leading with sound, and thinking about what sound from within each of these areas looks and feels like.

It is first pertinent to ask some *really* basic questions about sound design that rarely get answered, or indeed, even asked. The first of which is why do we need sounds in a game at all?

What is it that sounds bring when added to the interactive space and image? Is there an unquestionable necessity behind sound being present? Is it there solely for player feedback, and information, or is their more? Are there some habitual and inherited ideas about the use of sound in video games that can be unpicked, and even approached afresh?

An interesting place to begin this line of thinking, is to consider the history of silent cinema, a period wherein for roughly the first *40 years* from the invention of moving pictures there was no way to reliably synchronize and reproduce sound along with that projected image. There were, however, a great many innovative ways of supplying sound, music and voice to the otherwise silent images of the screen during these 40 years. Some of these methods involved accompanying performers, moving picture orchestras, innovative keyboard instruments that doubled as sound and music effects spectacle, live operation of noise-making sound effects machinery, many even with live narration and song. This was an incredibly fertile period of niche invention and innovation, and very often the sound and performative element rivalled, and was often even more important, than the images being shown on the screen. The technology to *reliably* synchronize sound, that could be commercially propagated into cinemas only came by the very end of the 1920s in 1927, most famously with 'The Jazz Singer', though many other similar technologies were gaining traction at the time.[1]

With video games, there was never a *truly* silent period in anywhere near the same way that there was in cinema, at least never in the sphere of commercially available games. Even though rudimentary sound chips were seemingly always a part of the gaming experience and spectacle, and the distinctive sound quality and character of these early chip sounds still haunts video game sound in the popular imagination today. In every conceivable way, a truly *silent* aesthetic for video games would need to be one that was enforced for purely aesthetic reasons, rather than something that was imposed by technological ones – which in itself makes it an interesting proposition. This very notion of a silent aesthetic begins to open up scope for silent video games that function perfectly as games, perfectly playable and enjoyable by an audience, designed to operate without sound, and on those merits alone, by extension these could also be commercially successful. It isn't too much of a stretch of the imagination to similarly suggest that this could become a particularly interesting sub-genre of video game experiences, whereby audiences would need to supply their own sound, either through play, or imagination.

What would games be lacking, or gaining, by excluding sound?

One area to consider as being affected by the removal of all sound is that of *immersion* in a precisely and meticulously defined sound world, vs *engagement* in a more loosely defined world. Having a player *engaged* in the game (rather than 'immersed'), a player who is able to think freely without the influence of the imposed meaning and emotion of sounds, without the feedback and interaction of synchronous and asynchronous sound effects to further deliver narrative or materially encoded information to the player – there suddenly opens up an enormous space, one of independence and freedom for the player in a silent game. This gaming experience, though only theoretical, could be perhaps likened in engagement terms to the act of reading a novel. There are no sound effects, music or voice-over accompanying a novel, though there may of course be the suggestions and mention of all of those things encoded in the text of the book. In the act of reading a novel, these sounds, of characters voices, or scenes, are then rendered by the mind of the reader into the sonic imagination. Similarly, board or card games carry with them no soundtracks or aesthetically defined sonic accompaniment, other than perhaps the sounds of the flicking and shuffling of the cards themselves, or the rolling of dice. By handing over to the player authorship of the 'sound' of the silent video game, the player is freed from what could, from a certain perspective, be described as a tyranny of designed sound in modern video game experiences. A tyranny which dictates a specific and often singular stylistically pre-defined *reading* of the game world and story. In silent games, there is infinite bandwidth and space for interpretation, and for discussion with other participants in the case of multiplayer games. Arguably, there would be more scope for players to decide to supply their own creative input, for instance by listening to their own music or sounds in the background as they play, as well as perhaps narrating and role playing the experience themselves 'in character', and so on (a form of this already occurs in games that have no dialogue, but only text). A more participatory and imaginary gameplay experience could therefore be proposed by making room for this player, or audience supplied sound: the creation of space for the audience, the encouragement of imaginary sound to be supplied by the players, in the vacuum left behind by the removal of the commission, designed sound, cast and performed voices and composed music.

There is absolutely no reason why silent games as a genre could not have a valid place in video games today. The question then becomes, what then does the *inclusion* of sound bring to the experience of interactive entertainment, more specifically, designed and managed sound effects.

The pleasure of immersion

The necessity of sound in (non-silent) games could be described quite simply as the conveyance of information coupled with the pleasures of immersion. Sound is a particularly sensorial phenomenon, and one in which it can be pleasurable to immerse yourself as a player, whether that pleasure is specific to the dictates and expectations of genre (horror, fantasy or sci-fi) or whether it is pure simulation (Battlefield, Formula 1 racing and so on) to the pleasures of a narrative cinematic experience. To a high degree in games, the player is able to suspend their disbelief in the constructed artifice of the world being presented to them, and by having sound effects playback as expected in synchronization with the actions of the player on screen, a certain convincing physical normalcy of cause and effect is established. Escapism plays a big role in almost all forms of entertainment media, from the novel to the radio play to cinema and ultimately into video games or VR experiences, in which we as players can control some of the outcomes of what we see and hear on screen. Perhaps the more pleasurable a simulated reality is for the player, the more engagement and immersion there is in the escapism.

A great deal of this convincing reality comes through the synchronous effect of sound, or appropriate and expected sound, playing in synchronisation with the image and action initiated on screen by the player. Foley and physics based-spot effects all play a role in providing a stage for the player to 'test' the expected reality of the world and the sound that is triggered through interaction with it. This can also be referred to as sandbox gameplay, in which the player is offered the opportunity to try anything in the world, to test the boundaries and rules of the simulation, often encouraging the most extreme possible activities up to the player. Having sounds that adapt and scale to match what is being triggered on-screen is an essential part of this modelling. If the sounds do not match what is expected onscreen, then the suspension of disbelief can be easily broken, and the engagement of the player diminished.

This kind of sound synchronisation to actions onscreen can also be extended to UI sound, and the expectation that some kind of sound feedback should accompany the player's navigational actions as they move through the options. Accompanying and satisfyingly appropriate sound effects that retain the style and genre expectations of the game are expected in the UI navigation and menu sounds that are triggered by the player. There are relatively few parallels for this in the real world, other than perhaps operating a keyboard, or analog switchboard for a machine (such as an old tape machine) where buttons, switches and dials make reassuring affirmatory clicks and pings. As we move into digital interface design, some of this same sound re-enforcement has followed as a necessary ingredient to *feedback*, signalling that an option had been made or a setting status chosen. *Without* the sound, it would be difficult for the user to have confidence in the interface selection. These influences usually culminate into a video game UI sound design which is an amalgamation of the product design feedback and Hollywood imaginings into what such interfaces could sound like in the future. There is no better representation of the exaggerated presence of sound than in the sci-fi genre and it's imagined sounds of the interfaces of the future – though mostly the reality of such futuristic interfaces is one in which all is silent. A case in point is the iPhone's touch interface and navigation experience which is entirely silent – if such an interface were to appear in a sci-fi movie then this would certainly have had swiping and clicking sounds added. The sounds in any case are, or should be, giving us both feedback information and sensual satisfaction (not irritation), in equal measure.

In a similar sense, the pleasure of heightened emotion and exaggerated sound to accompany events onscreen and off, is something that we as audiences are used to in the presentation of the dramatic events of Hollywood blockbuster cinema. *Hollywood* – this species of exaggerated psychological realism is one that has been readily adopted in games, and perhaps become even more exaggerated. The very essence of the roller-coaster-ride-like experience of action cinema and action adventure video games is one in which exaggeration, and the distinct presence of tension and release are carefully plotted and planned to deliver optimal thrill. It is the implication that the player or central character is a form of super-listener that can perceive both minutely detailed quiet sounds, as well as hearing the loudest sounds of unrelenting gun shots, jet engines and nuclear explosions in a clean and undistorted way (a super-human SPL range not possible in human hearing without sustaining damage) – just as in Dolby-era[2] cinema sound, the realities of human hearing are conveniently left behind in favour of foregrounding the pleasurable, sensual and the dramatic.

Sound games then, are driven by and reliant upon these pleasures in order to engage their audiences. The expectations of the audience of games to experience thematic material presented in a way which is received as an extension of a *popular entertainment continuum* which includes all popular forms of entertainment culture: cinema, theatre, music video and TV in general. Games have joined the stream of this continuum with relative ease, and even though they are heavily influenced by movies, have themselves become *influencers* on this continuum – even affecting how movies, theatre and music videos are made and consumed (using run-time video game engines for pre-visualization on set), edited (faster paced cuts) and received (streamed or downloaded in the home entertainment ecosystem) as an augmentation to, *not replacement of*, the reception point of the cinema theatre. Because of the establishment and use of so many narrative conventions, it is possible to already understand and know much of what an audience might *expect* from a game's soundtrack by benchmarking Hollywood action or similar genre movies to the game that you are perhaps making. It is a process of piecing together the most usable elements of these expectations and seeing where they can be tweaked in order to push the experience and pleasure of the game even further. Or perhaps seeing where a unique ingredient can be used to take an already established genre and push it even further into unique territory.

Sound is so important in games for a great many reasons, not least of which is the amount of extra information that sound carries about the world, the story and the characters in the game. In one single package a sound can deliver information, entertainment and immersion. Sound can give us information far beyond what is simply onscreen, and it can even offer the audience different, and contrary ways of interpreting an image. Inviting an ambiguous reading of an image, through the addition of sound, can open the door to exciting possibilities for a storytellers and audiences, bringing in mystery or suspicion to a scene, perhaps adding ambiguity to something that, on the surface might appear to be ordinary. Sound then brings with it not only an entire world, but the possibility of other private or mysterious worlds underneath the one we may be looking at. Not only worlds alive with sound, but alive with the sounds and psychological murmurings of the inner worlds of the characters *within* the world we see onscreen.

9 Working with sound

Building from nothing: the importance of rules

The idea of starting with nothing, with just a silent canvass, is at once exciting, exhilarating and terrifying. All things are possible until a first sound is made. Ideally, we are quick to discover the need for a creative frame within which to work and get started on this blank page. This frame could be also thought of in terms of a set of rules, or instructions that can determine what is and is not possible to grow into this silence.

In this chapter we will examine some methods for helping to design sounds and establishing a solid and understandable creative frame, and also why it is important to have a rule-based system, and also how important it is to define and set out a unique and memorable aesthetic that can be applied and understood by anyone working on the sound content for a title or franchise.

Establishing limits

As mentioned in the previous chapters in regard to an overall approach for a project, coming up with the rules, or understanding the rules that have already been set on a project's creative vision or game direction, can often take a while and probably the best way to achieve a clear understanding of them is to test them and put together examples in a variety of situations.

The reason for creating these kinds of limitations and rules is fairly straightforward. In a very competitive marketplace where originality and novelty is highly valuable, being able to differentiate one video game project from the next is extremely important for an audience. The goal is to have a sound signature style (visual artistic direction is built in exactly the same way with rules and limits that define a visual brand) – one that is ideally instantly identifiable, and potentially even *ownable* by the game or the franchise that you are working on.

Creative boundaries are not often referred to as 'rules' – they may be referred to by a wide variety of other names, such as pillars, principles and so on, in order to feel more like guidelines and recipes within a creative framework, and let's face it, nobody likes rules. This approach is important for music and voice but *especially* pertinent for sound design, as it is an area that is often negatively impacted by the freely available nature of many pre-designed sound effects that can simply be found in a library and applied to a scene quickly at the last minute without taking the time to understand if the sound really fits the overall tone. Understanding the overall aesthetic will exclude a lot of pre-made sounds, and instead necessitate a degree of specifically recorded and designed material for the project in order to get exactly the unique identity required. Much of this sound recording and source sound gathering occurs in the early days of the project. Because of this, it is useful to have some early working version of the sound principles worked out and demonstrable so that location scouting for sound recording or reference gathering trips can be organised in advance. There is almost zero chance that there will be time, budget or inclination to go out and record very specific sounds once production is fully underway and the priorities of the work have shifted towards the fast execution of sound in the game engine – not that it isn't possible to do it later in the day, but that the *opportunity* to spend the right amount of time needed to plan, arrange, record and catalogue the sounds required for a unique project is one that really should not be squandered.

To help illustrate the point, I have devised some examples of guiding sound principles for an invented sci-fi franchise.

Sound principle example: for an invented horror sci-fi game

Principle 1 Establish Authenticity. Even though we are in a futuristic sci-fi setting, we must always feel that what we experience is possible and relatable. Realistic reverbs and physics sound reactions must always be appropriate matching the surroundings. The establishing of a concrete and believable reality will be extremely important later when we start to contrast that, and introduce horror sounds that cannot possibly be real.

Principle 2 Broken and Unreliable Tech. Every sound of technology (ships, weapons, consoles) should reveal a slightly broken and patched together reality – nothing in this sci-fi world should be pristine, it should be old, broken, leaky, rusty, hacked – the inner workings of the machines and objects that the player interacts with should all feel as though they are about to break, or have been repaired already many times. The reason for this is to create a world of tension, the player should always be thinking that the technology they rely on might not work correctly, if at all. This is not the glossy white silent future of 2001 a Space Odyssey, but more the rust and filth of the trash compactor in Star Wars.

Principle 3 Ambiguity. Non-diegetic sounds that we never see the cause of, and never understand where they come from, should be heard increasingly throughout the game. This is done to introduce confusion and tension, so that the player sometimes doubts the reality of what they hear, but also allows them to *imagine* that the things causing the sounds are the things that scare them the most. These sounds can be either in the realm of the realistic (a faulty air duct, strange falling metal pipes in another room, or door malfunctioning and slamming shut or creaking with movement from other rooms) or from the realms of the psychological – whispers, distant, almost musical under-tones and drones, as well as sounds that are un-relatable and have no known original in reality, and that could be emanating from inside the player's head or nervous system (blood circulation etc.).

There are often three principles. I don't know why, but most creative pillar systems (though obviously not all) seem to triangulate quite nicely. It also reflects a little the categorisation of sounds discussed earlier in the book, where sound can be thought about as either objective (world), intellectual (mind) or emotional (heart). Not all principles need to satisfy these three contexts, but it can come in useful if they inhabit each of these areas a little more than the others. For example, the authenticity element in the above example could represent our objective sound approach, the broken tech could be our intellectual element, and the ambiguity could represent the emotional and psychological fear aspect.

10 Higher level is better

The three examples from the previous chapter are very useful, and we could start making some sounds based on these, but I really need to boil these down into even higher-level principles that can be easily remembered and communicated by everyone, not just on the sound team. To do that I am going to reduce them to one word each. *Authentic. Unreliable. Ambiguous.* Now I have these three words, I can memorise these and be ready to talk about and apply these principles to all kinds of design situations or conversations, and also during reviews of sound that I may have with my sound team. I can use these principles to push the sound in any one or more of these directions. The really great thing is, you can stand up in any meeting and dramatically write these down on a white board, and then start to talk about what they mean.

What also happens with simple high-level principles is that they can become quickly adopted throughout the entire team as a familiar and easily memorable part of the project's vision. If other departments, such as art or animation, can also get on familiar conversational terms with the sound principals, and even adopt some of them as though they were their own principles, or merge them into the discussion of their own discipline-specific aesthetic discussions and reviews, then the influence of the sound world of the game becomes more active.

Freedom to interpret the rules

Another advantage of reducing the principles down to single words, as broad concepts, is that they can then be *interpreted*. An interpretation of a principle is a way by which the spirit of the principle may be respected, but the implementation of it may be very specifically tailored to something that still works from a practical standpoint of a low-level feature.

To give an example, we might be working on a weapon sound in our sci-fi game example and we find ourselves under pressure to make the weapons in the game feel much larger than life to satisfy tense combat. The design department is pushing to give the player better feedback and satisfaction about the type of weapon they are using as well as the amount of damage the weapon is doing on the enemy in fights after having received some feedback in a play-test to that effect. This brings about some conflicts with the sound design because it is using the first principle, authenticity, to create weapon sounds that are based on the realistic, unglamorous sounds of firing real weapons. The initial reaction to the feedback may be to adopt another approach such as may be expected in a blockbuster Hollywood movie sci-fi (like 'Blade Runner') where a weapon is only fired meaningfully in one or two instances in the entire movie but sounds beefy and impactful. In our game, the weapons the player has are fired *all the time*, and can be fired at *any* time, and therefore quickly lose impact and meaning.

We may decide that our third principle, that of *ambiguity* is one which can come more heavily into play here. What if the weapon is a representation not *entirely* of the authenticity of the world, but also of the ambiguity of the psychological state of the player character, of the paranoia reflective of being in this world... we could add a new layer to the weapon firing sounds which drastically increases the low-end transient of the firing sounds in order to make each shot feel more powerful, but *only* in very stressful or high-combat moments: figuring out some way of the weapon sound changing over time depending on the situation (psychologically speaking) has the distinct advantage of making the sound more reactive and dynamic as we go through the story and the experience. We also do not lose our authentic sound design angle that was generally felt to be working well on the team.

The important thing at the end of this is to make sure in the next playtest that the participants are asked about the new weapon feel.

We are able to navigate and interpret those three one-word principles in order to consider their relation to one another, we are able to navigate the challenge to the principles according to specific feature feedback, and in each instance we can push or pull one element further than the other.

In doing this kind of exercise, or in applying principles in this way on a real project, you may see that it helps considerably to have principles that almost contradict one another, or that describe and occupy very different opposing corners of the sound world's objective, intellectual and emotional experience.

Freedom to break the rules

Of course, sometimes, even interpreting the rules in a way that pushes the principals in contradictory directions will not solve every instance of feedback or iteration. It can, on occasion, be necessary to fully and deliberately break the rules, and it is perfectly fine to do this. The principles are there to guide you through decision making and evaluation on a project, they are there to provide you with tools and lenses that are specific to your creative vision, with which you can review content and make logical suggestions and adjustments. But a game will sometimes throw up something that is entirely necessary to the experience, but is outside of the established scope and remit. A good example is usually found in a flashback or a dream sequence – perhaps a playable one (rather than just a short non-interactive movie sequence). In the case where you have built the principles around a location (on a spaceship) around a specific set of objective and psychological principles, and then there is a playable level in a dream, where the location changes to a country house (in the character's childhood). This level / map may not be something that was ever discussed or planned in the early concept or pre-production areas of the project but has come up as a necessary aspect of the story that now means it has become pivotally important to the game's story. Obviously, in a dream sequence set in a county house on earth, none of our sci-fi principles apply – authenticity might not hold up if we want to sell the vividness of the dream and exaggerate the sounds. The principle of unreliability also won't apply, because everything in this dream is organic, and not mechanical, it is a dream in the countryside after all, an escape from the 'established cold reality of the real and unreliable world of the ship'. Ambiguity may also not quite work, because in the dream, there isn't the need for the usual horror techniques we've been using of playing weird sounds that don't belong in the scene and come from outside the physical space that the player is in. We basically *want* this whole sequence to feel different, and to be a complete opposite to the established rules and tone of the game so far. So it really is necessary to deliberately break all of the rules and guidelines in this instance.

Of course, all of this still 'works' in the game, because what is happening here is that all the rules are being suspended, or broken, momentarily for dramatic purposes. No longer applying all those principles is necessary in order for this scene to work. It is a much needed and necessary pattern breaker from what is expected in the game and narrative.

The use of pattern breakers such as this are quite prevalent in games, as the repetitive action and detectable recipes, and often repetitive locations of gameplay, are very quick to become noticeable and annoying to the player. So, an occasional and deliberate rule break can also offer a release from the formulas of some games. This can be done in very obvious ways, like the aforementioned dream sequence, or it can be done in much more subtle ways to accommodate designs or requirements that are outside of the principles that have been established. Whatever the case, the systems you build, cannot be immune to these kinds of unpredictable elements outside of the definitions of your system.

Systems, Story and Emotions

In games, worlds are often built from systems and recipes that will run as a simulation. This is a particularly important architectural feature in more exploration-based titles, such as open world or similarly very large games which have open player choice across vast landscapes – pure simulation or 'sandbox' games are constructed largely of these rules and systems and mostly do not have a strong story element to contend with. In these kinds of games, once a story comes into play, all those systems are going to need to either work perfectly *with* the story that is being told (in the case of a story that is made to use the systems of the game), or the systems need to bend to the will of that story in order to give the player the contexts required as they change over the arc of the story.

Some examples of systemic sounds necessary for the auto-population and propagation of sound object triggers throughout a game's world are as follows...

- Time of day (switching or transitioning sounds based on morning, day, evening, night etc.)
- Season or location (methods of switching the sounds used to accommodate different seasons or dramatically different biomes based on geographical location)
- Ambience (both 3D positional elements as well as more general quad or static backgrounds that are auto populated based on the type of biome)
- Physics sounds (sound systems that trigger audio events based on material, scale and velocity of physics objects)
- Weapons (devising systems by which weaponry can be switched or customized by a player, with the appropriate sounds accompanying them based on which component is customised or equipped by the player)
- Foley (systems by which the movement sounds of a character, or characters, are modified based on what clothing or gear the character has equipped, which is often modifiable by the player)
- Reverb (systemic reverb may also be something that is applied using the games geometry to calculate appropriate reverb zones that have the correct amount of reflection, and even take into consideration the sound absorption values and properties of the materials that the walls are made of, to colour the reflection type and decay time).

These all represent entire sets and systems of sounds that are developed to be shared and propagated throughout an *entire game* from start to finish, thus making it a lot easier to manage sounds across massive game experiences with many hours of gameplay.

However, many things can adversely affect these kinds of systems from a higher level. A simulation, or system design, usually only takes into account one point of view or one objective world viewpoint of those system sounds. But in games with multiple characters who hear the game with a different POV (Point of view) or whose POV changes over the course of a story or native arc, these systems need to accommodate for that kind of dynamic perspective modification. Characters hear things that are important to them, and important to the story. If characters are switchable dynamically speaking, and the POV is a simple modification (for example a character with extremely good hearing) then we might now need to apply weighting to the overall sound based on character selection – in the case of a *super-hearing* character, we could play back all the same content, but have a different kind of attenuation curve on sounds that are deemed to be early signs of a threat (such as enemy footsteps). This would mean that when the game is played with that particular character, the sound design adapts based on the character's POV.

If we step into more story-driven examples, whereby a character's POV changes throughout the narrative *arc* of the main story, then we can similarly apply these kinds of tweaks, though it is more likely that, in a story-driven experience, the priority of what is the most important sound will be unsupported by a systemic design. For example, one single footstep at a very specific moment needs to be audible from a far distance at a specific one-off moment in the story. In this instance we could simply *script* a one-off single footstep, outside of the footstep system, to do that narrative work. These are often referred to as scripted, or one-off unique sound moments or perspectives.

So, while we may have created, or set out to create, what we assume to be a solid, rule-based audio system for our game world that matches and takes into account all the parameters that the design team has told us about, we will surely find that either the story, or additional characters or new POV perspectives, at various times, need to subvert or override those systems in order to convey different emotion and information pertinent to those situations.

Stories are not very interesting or engaging if they are predictable and repetitive, so they will always aim to surprise both the player, and you, the developer. Provided the way to override these systems has been considered during the design stage, then the way to get the story content to play nice with them is going to be fairly trivial via scripting. By always considering ways to override your systems, you are making sure that surprises brought about by story changes, or any other kind of necessity, can be more easily achieved, and more importantly, you are preparing your teams mentally for this kind of eventuality, and can spare them some of the turmoil of having to defend a system over a story decision, which is inevitably going to cause argument and frustration, and invariably the story will win.

Whatever the proposed disruption is to the system, having some resilience build into your approach is essential.

11 What is causing these sounds and where are they located?

Diegetic, non-diegetic and trans-diegetic sound

Understanding where a sound source is located in your game is an often over-looked element in many approaches to sound design – quite frequently, the sound design itself is conceived and attended to in great detail, but very little of the context of sound propagation through the spatial environment to the ears of the listener is considered. It may just be left to the rules and systems of the sound world to take care of all of this environmental playback information, but there is *much* more to consider about these sound source contexts.

Where the sound occurs, provides both spatial contexts, and meaning. Not only is understanding the vernacular of the sound storytelling in the game world an essential part of the storytelling toolkit, but also understanding the degree to which spatial and causal clarity and ambiguity comes into play for each sound source.

Fortunately, sound sources can be broken down into some very simple zones, all of which have interesting ramifications for whether the source of the sound we actually hear in the game is in the scene and visible by the player, in the scene and not visible, or if it perhaps emanates from outside of that scene. There are broad layers of how far away a sound is, as well as how filtered through the emotional and psychological lenses of the characters that sound is, and of course if the sound itself is entirely imagined and outside of the proposed onscreen game world entirely. Players of 3D games are especially used to attending to their 3D environment and taking these kinds of informational and emotional cues from the sounds they hear. Sound sources can also dynamically move between all of these different zones, and we will understand that in almost all gameplay narratives, and storytelling with sound, that sounds in games are continually trans-diegetic, and trans-contextual in nature. A sound is never just a sound, it is a sound within a context.

Diegetic and non-diegetic sound

The simple definition of whether a sound is onscreen (in the world) or offscreen (outside of the world) needs to be expanded considerably when talking about game environments.

We can meditate quite precisely on where the proposed sources of sounds are in games, as so much sound that we hear in games is technically 'offscreen' due to the nature of having the player in control of the camera, especially in 3D games. A player can choose to look at whatever they like in a full sphere of vision, continually re-framing what is onscreen and what is off. When this happens, we do not expect the objects in the 3D scene to stop making sound when they move behind the camera (though we may expect a reduction in the 'focus' of those less important sounds so that events that are to the side or behind or above the player are attenuated slightly lower).

Thinking about the diegetic sound in a 3D game in rings that emanate outwards from the player's position is a good way to start to describe these different 'bands' of diegetic sound (see figure 11.1).

Immediate diegetic sound: seen sound

This category describes a sound in the game world that is *onscreen* and can be seen and heard by the player in the immediate environment: objects, or movement in the near field of view, that can be seen and thus expect a synchronised sound effect. For example: falling rocks from a cliff – we see the rocks fall and expect there to be an accompanying and appropriate rock falling sound, as well as the expected amount of reverberant reflection from the surrounding

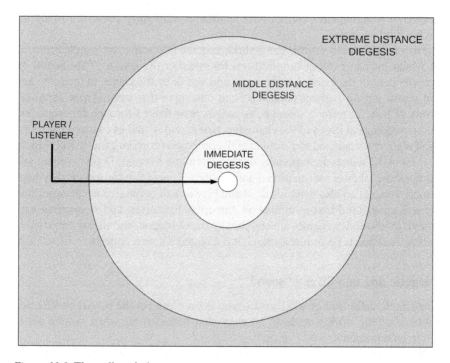

Figure 11.1 Three diegetic layers

environment. If our camera is pointing towards these rocks, then we will see the rocks and expect to hear the sound positioned directly ahead of us. If our camera is pointing away from the rocks, then the event is triggered, we still hear the rocks falling behind us, and may now turn the camera around to see the cause of these sounds, and expect to see the tail end of the rocks falling, or some kind of remnant dust trail.

Immediate diegetic sound without a visual source

Games can also exploit the idea of sounds that are diegetic, being produced in the immediate environment that is observed onscreen, however, there may be no visual asset which to attribute the onscreen cause for these sounds. For example: we see a dense jungle or forest onscreen, with lots of foliage, and we hear many birds, frogs and amphibians in 3D all around us, perhaps even flies and mosquitos. However, not one single bird, frog or fly is rendered visually in the game, just the dense foliage. Technically this could be defined as offscreen sound by having no onscreen cause, but it is still considered to be sound that is *proposed to exist in the immediate diegesis*, and therefore belongs as much to the world, as anything rendered on screen. In fact, these sound objects are usually treated in entirely the same way as if they were attached to objects on screen – just that they are 'sound objects' with no visual element.

Middle distant (implied) diegesis

As we push the idea of diegetic sounds without onscreen sources further out from the player, we encounter sounds in the middle distant diegesis. Again, this is an area of the world onscreen that is not being visually rendered but is being implied and extrapolated by the sound field we might hear. As an example: if we consider that same jungle or forest environment, but then add to that a series of very distant sounds, perhaps of an industrial factory drone, a player can infer that beyond the dense forest that we can see, there is a factory or processing plant of some kind. We may recognise such factory sounds from earlier in the story, if they are iconic and recognisable, and therefore know that this is somewhere to either avoid (because it proved dangerous) or pursue (because we know this is where we need to go). Of course, the factory is not rendered in the game engine yet, it does not exist, not being streamed or loaded until we get much closer, and the sound we hear may be treated in such a way as to imply that it is even more distant, through use of filters, or increased reverb reflections, as well as a more diffuse and blurry 3D positioning in space (a slightly more 'spread' sound source). Nonetheless, this is a sound that we could use to orient ourselves in the dense forest environment, and therefore move in the desired direction accordingly. Of course, a sound in the middle distance may, after some time of moving towards it, shift to the immediate view in front of the player, and may be treated to a 'reveal moment' scripted camera when it finally appears onscreen. At this point our sound source is revealed, and a visual connection between sound and sight is made, and the cause revealed. The sound has also now moved into the immediate diegesis.

Extreme distant (implied) diegesis

There may also be sounds coming from much further beyond the middle distance, into what may be referred to as the extreme distant diegesis. These could be caused by sound events of extremely loud volume that are detectable over great distances and are therefore audible by the listener. For example, in the forest we hear very distant thunder, even though there is no rain in our immediate environment; we could assume that a storm is approaching, we may even get a distant vista shot reveal of a very distant rainstorm. Similarly, enormous explosions occurring in the extreme distance: For example, a distant city is being ravaged and destroyed by an alien invasion, and we are aware of those events through hearing the occasional low rumble of distant destruction. We may simply see all this as a distant plume of black smoke on the horizon. These sounds are still very much a part of the diegesis, and the world proposed to the player on screen. Even though their visual sources are not rendered, and do not exist at all, but are implied.

Ethereal diegesis (radio)

Another element of diegetic sound (sound whose cause is emanating from the game world) that is often present in video games is that of radio dialogue, or radio sound. Radio and telephone are both technologies whereby the sound and cause of that sound may be broadcast over vast distances *to* our lister position. This kind of voice or sound transmission is often used to communicate information to the player via the dialogue of an offscreen character. A character who is using this method of communication may be known to the player from the beginning or may be someone they eventually meet during the course of the story, or maybe someone who it is impossible to meet (the voice of an artificial intelligence like Cortana for example). This category of ethereal broadcast diegesis therefore needs to exist in order to explain the method of sound being produced that the player character can hear, and whose cause is a long distance away.

If we consider all of these diegetic bands together, beginning with what can be seen in the immediate environment and moving outwards to sounds in the middle distance, and outwards father still into the extreme distance, we can begin to build a model and talk about sound as being transitional between these layers, or we can also consider them to be three *storytelling* bands of sound that we could consider having an approach for in every location or scene in the game.

Non-diegetic sound

Non-diegetic sound, that which is not a part of the onscreen world and does not have an originating sound source or event in the world should also be considered. Typically, this refers to sounds that are not produced in the environment or game world, but are emanating from the consciousness, or sub-consciousness of the character or player – or are simply not explained and exist to induce an element of excitement or anxiety in the player. As mentioned previously, 'non-diegetic sound' can sometimes refer to simply anything 'off-screen', but as games allow a camera to move around and simply locate sounds that are offscreen or navigate towards them, the term non-diegetic for me as it applies to games needs to refer more specifically to sounds that are *not caused in the world onscreen*.

Musical score is the most often used example of a type of non-diegetic sound, being a sound that the audience can hear, but that the characters in the world cannot. We do not expect characters in the game world to react to hearing the score – and we do not expect to find musicians in the game world creating the music we hear in the score – but let's consider some potential examples of 'sound' that does not emanate from the world itself.

diegetic layers

Non-diegetic sound refers to sound that has no inferable cause or location in the 3D game world. For example: a low frequency drone-like sound that we hear quite frequently in a sci-fi game in which we are exploring an old space station. The sound is not referenced by any of the characters in the world, nobody seems to 'hear it' or react to it, but it is there to represent the uneasiness of how the characters feel at certain moments. It is a sound that even the players may not immediately notice that they are hearing. The cause and the 3D location of the sound is never revealed to the player in a way that enables them to find it. It is there to create an uneasy mood, and perhaps eventually functions as an indicator or foreshadowing of some unpleasant event that is upcoming in the narrative. The distinction between this kind of sound, and the score, could become one of contention, as sounds are very much being used here in the same ways that music score is traditionally used. Perhaps the sound does have a vague sense of 3D positionally in the game world, although even that could be made ambiguous with a lot of diffuse spread obscuring a precise location. However, these sounds are absolutely not music, or musical, at least not in the sense that they have been written and composed for this purpose by a composer.

Another way of thinking about this category of sound is to consider it as imagined 'ambiguous sound' – sound that *could* be emanating from within the world, perhaps at the limits of the middle-distance or extreme distance of the diegesis - but at the same time its source could entirely be the imagination of the character or player. What we hear, as players, could be the interpretation of a distant sound, a more 'designed' version of real world sound, but used in a way to communicate the psychology of the characters and what *they* hear rather than the objective sound itself as it would expect to be heard. The category of ambiguous sound is one that seems to be ever expanding in its use in games, especially where the psychology and inner world of the characters is in question or in flux – and even where the music scores themselves, while still operating in the non-diegetic 'space' of a traditional score - are partly entering the world of ambiguous sound through use of texture or more concrete, less recognisable musical sources.

Trans-diegetic sound

Ambiguous sound that eventually has its cause revealed is one example of an area where sound begins as non-diegetic, established as a mystery, and is eventually revealed to be a part of the diegesis – for the purposes of the narrative, the sound has remained unexplained, or if referred to by the characters at all, it is done so in terms whereby the characters themselves are either unsure of the reality of the sound, or are all hearing different things and interpreting the sound in a way that reveals their inner psychology along the way. The eventual unveiling of these kinds of ambiguous sounds, by assuming proximity to a source, or by bringing the cause into the immediate diegesis, and having the characters confront it, completes the transition from non-diegetic (in the imagination of the characters) to diegetic, something revealed in the game world that can be seen and has a concrete reality, and which now renders the mystery solved.

Sounds may also obviously transition quite freely between the various diegetic zones as seen in the figure 11.1. An important contextual element is whether a sound has been introduced to the player already or not. If a sound begins by being in the immediate diegesis – and the source is clearly visible and identifiable by the player – when this sound recedes offscreen into the middle distance, or the extreme distance, the 'known cause' of that sound is still held in the player's mind, and can be referenced continuously without seeing the cause.

If on the other hand, the cause of a sound is not revealed or introduced, then the sound will have a degree of ambiguity *until* that cause is revealed. During this time, the listener will be searching for meaning in what they hear, and if the mystery of this sound is a feature of the story, then this can work very powerfully. All this describes the motion of meaning around trans-diegetic sound.

Certain sounds could also be initially known or ambiguous to audiences for cultural reasons, such as the types of birds heard in the Amazon jungle. A listener not familiar with those environments would likely not understand what caused those sounds as they are quite alien to a European or North American ear – while someone *familiar* with that environment, who would understand these cues and be at once familiar with their source, would infer correctly the birds associated with those sounds. This cultural element is something to be aware of when building the meaning in the soundtrack terms of clarity and ambiguity. The sound of howler monkeys for example, is an unusual, and sometimes quite disturbing to the ear of someone unfamiliar with them. The sound can have an almost horror-movie like feel to it when you don't know what this sound is.

The important element here is the degree to which you understand what sounds are going to make sense to an audience (either culturally, or through narrative exposition) and which sounds are going to be ambiguous and mysterious to a player, and how, or even if, they are going to be resolved.

12 Ambiguity and clarity

These two areas of sound, and the oscillation between them, of being clear, and of being unknown or mysterious, are another of the key storytelling and world-immersing tools of sound in games. Sound has great potential to deliver on both of these in powerful ways, and a lot of storytelling works on an emotional and subconscious level by playing with the degree to which a sound is recognisable, or understandable or not. The degree to which sound needs to be clear or ambiguous will depend entirely on the storytelling and world building of your game. But this idea will connect back to your overall rules, pillars and vision for the project. Whether the initial sounds you made highlight mysterious sounds, or whether they occur with vivid clarity a specific and relatable scene, you are setting up and establishing very different ways in which sound is being used to communicate the game to the team and eventually the audience. How much is the game experience about mystery or a sense of eeriness? How much of it is about absolute clarity? These are very big topics to be understood.

On a more practical level, understanding the pathways along which your sounds will move from ambiguity to clarity, or from clarity to ambiguity, can also help to understand the overall game, or story, from a variety of new perspectives, that will all ultimately, and potentially very deeply, influence the ways in which you implement the sound and the mix for the game.

Stillness, not silence

Another major ingredient in sound design is creating contrasts and dynamics with the absence of sound. Silence is often thrown around as a concept, however, in almost all cases where the word silence is evoked in discussions, what is actually being thought about is a similar, but entirely different concept... *stillness*. In thinking about the concepts of silence and stillness, I think the far more useful and practical storytelling device of *stillness* is a more precise term for explaining the feeling that we wish to express onscreen.

To give an example, imagine that we are in a game world and walking through a sparse and cold Northern European forest environment. The sounds of birds and frogs are busy and active all around us, after a while our ears stop paying direct attention to these ever-present ambient sounds, and we begin to accept them as a constant background state of the forest. Then, perhaps almost imperceptibly at first, the mood begins to change. The sky darkens a little, and some segments of the bird population no longer seem to be present. Birds in our immediate proximity no longer seem to be making sounds at all, and only distant birds in the middle or extreme distance appear to be audible now, and certainly less frequently. Frogs now also no longer seem to chirp with the constant enthusiasm they used to, reduced to an occasional chirp. A twig breaks nearby, suddenly very noticeable. Only the sounds of the insects continue, but even they, as the sky continues to darken, and the temperature seems to drop, start to become less present, like gradually slowing tiny clockwork toys. We now feel the *stillness* of the forest, distant sound still occasionally is audible, it seems that we can hear much 'further' away than before, our hearing is focussing on perhaps a very distant dog barking, or a motorbike passing by in the extreme distance. Life continues outside this area of the forest seemingly as normal, but here, things are not as they should be, they are still. As the stillness continues, we start to notice now more micro-sounds, drips of water, tiny little creaking sounds of branches, the Foley sound and detail of our footsteps seems all the more present and focussed, even loud – you have the feeling that these sounds may be alerting anything nearby to your precise location. Then suddenly… *it attacks!*

The way this scene would typically be described to us, perhaps in a pitch meeting, at the proposal stage, is that 'as we walk through a forest, "everything goes silent", just before a creature attacks the player in a jump-scare moment'. To take that reference to silence literally is a mistaken interpretation that can occur all too often. Perhaps rather than take the time and energy to fully orchestrate the slow invasion of stillness on the environment that I described above, we need to test this idea very quickly in the most raw and sketchy way possible. In the case of fast prototyping, I think perhaps silence can be acceptable, we could kill all the ambient sound and try out the idea, which is really about orchestrating a jump-scare. But really getting an audience, who we are asking to listen ever more carefully to the sound design in our games, to *buy into this* when done bluntly through the binary 'sound/no sound' of silence, is something that will rarely work without feeling that the sound in the game is broken and buggy. In my example, we are orchestrating and making space for the player to listen differently, to approach the environment differently and to question their movements and actions in that environment differently – we are authoring a moment, full of potential, into which something can *happen*.

Stillness is something that sometimes requires this kind of detailed and deliberate orchestration, or more accurately a process of de-orchestration of a soundscape, and can be an extremely powerful concept in terms of getting a player to explore deeper with their ears, and to lean in and listen more carefully or more actively to interactive environments. Stillness also allows a player, through listening, to 'reach' further into the distant diegesis of the environment – reaching for more remote or distant points than they would normally expect to be able to hear. A sense of stillness could also be something that is conjured through removal of excessive background sound, exaggerating the focus on sounds that are important. This idea of 'focus' could also be something used as a gameplay mechanic, the more skilled your character becomes in a game, the more extreme their ability to focus on key or important sounds becomes in the dynamic mix, reflecting the characters' ability to pick out important information in any given soundscape.

In our world, where in our experience of reality to perceive silence is practically and theoretically impossible (from the quietest sounds of our blood vessels in an anechoic chamber, to the potentially ceaseless inner voices and sounds inside our imagination) silence onscreen is a challenging concept because we can never truly experience it.

Silence does have cinematic precedents and is still used quite often onscreen – sometimes it is used as a semiotic shortcut for a complete shutdown of the senses. Yet, there always seems to be *some* abstract sound, music or voice present in these cinematic moments of digital silence. Stillness, whether inner stillness, or stillness in a world environment is a more practical way of thinking about a less busy and uncluttered moment of focus on emotion, or gameplay, in which the perspective and the environment itself may change to induce a change of psychological state.

The vast and beautiful topic of stillness is explored in greater and considerably more poetic depth in Seán Street's book *The Sound Inside the Silence*. [1] In one of the earlier sections of the book, Seán is quick to introduce the reader to some of the many different species of silence – such as the recognisable concept of 'peace and quiet' – being a 'period of time into which thought pours with fewer interruptions'. On stillness, Seán meditates...

> Many have debated as to whether or not actual silence exists at all; stillness on the other hand is perhaps easier to identify and a shortlist might begin with the following...
>
> The stillness of a place from which we come.
> The stillness we make and or create out of mood – an active form of expression.
> The stillness we recognize when we listen actively.
> The stillness that is always inside us.
>
> The last is important... it is the stillness of anticipation, of intense attention, of waiting for an answer.

Distant sound: philosophies and approaches

In the previous chapter we explored the notion of trans-diegetic sound and discussed the ideas of distant sounds having great potential for psychological value, through interpretation and misinterpretation, in storytelling and gameplay by engaging the imagination of the player through their ambiguity.

Hearing, or half-hearing, sounds without seeing or knowing their cause, and having those distant sounds become delayed, amplified and filtered through the landscape as they travel toward the listener opens up a huge area of storytelling through managed ambiguity.

Making use of this idea of distant sounds being ambiguous, without a definitive visible cause, is a powerful one in games because it is connected intimately to the idea of physical three-dimensional space and the environment in which the player is able to navigate and explore. Though we will touch in more detail later on the importance of spatial audio in storytelling and particularly in its function of encouraging the player to explore, we will currently focus on the uses of ambiguity in 3D sound on the state of mind of the character or player.[2]

An example of distant ambiguous sound

To explore the sound field of ambiguity, I'll give a fictitious example of a setting in an invented game. Our character is exploring an abandoned military complex, the place is a ruin and has been ravaged by a destructive event, many years have passed and nature has started to reclaim much of the environment, with plant life bursting through the walls, and animal life setting up home in many of the ruined rooms and exposed rafters. Our onscreen character is a hunter. Their backstory has been exposed a little in the run up to this scene as someone who suffered through the traumatic post-apocalyptic event which wiped out most of the population, including close members of their family. Having had to survive for many years, the character now finds themselves roaming and hunting this environment for food (deer, etc). During this scene, the character begins their journey to discover what actually happened and caused that apocalyptic event.

Our gameplay begins on an ordinary hunt, killing a few deer on the perimeter of the ruined compound. Then the character begins tracking something much bigger than usual inside a ruined compound. Much of the stealth gameplay of hunting is achieved by listening and quietly creeping though the environments, using geographic features to get occasionally to higher ground, and using a crossbow bolt to shoot the prey. The sound here inside the compound now becomes still in terms of ambience, we hear less wind in the grass, less bird sound, fewer insects, and we build up the stillness inside the compound. This enables sudden movements from neighbouring abandoned rooms to be noticeably audible as we disturb whatever it is we are hunting. We feel we are close, getting closer, and that we are stalking the prey. As a rhythm of creeping, then startling, and getting closer starts to build, we now hear something in the *far* distance. A scream-like sound. It is at once familiar, yet different, it is the sound we normally associate with the kill of a deer when *we* are hunting and have made a kill shot, however, we now hear it from a distant perspective, echoing and filtered around the environment. It also seems to be in more pain than usual, doesn't sound like the clean kill we are used to hearing... it continues and moves, echoing around the distant space from a generally unclear direction... wounded. Then stillness again. We get the feeling that something else is hunting in this environment. Then another scream, more distant this time, more human, though still animalistic. All this distant sound is taking our focus off the immediate environment around us onscreen and allowing the set-up of a moment where we are off-guard. But also, during that time, we are confronted with a lot of questions about what is causing those sounds – because we do not know what it is – our minds will supply any number of scenarios. Is it another human hunter on this same patch? Is it someone who is not as well trained as me, perhaps a young person? Hence the inability to properly kill the deer. Is the first kill we heard perhaps the same animal my own character was hunting? Or perhaps the thing my character thought it was hunting actually killed the deer? This bubble of tension, mystery and questions certainly now needs to be burst.

By creating an ambiguous sound out of a hunting rhythm that we already established in terms of gameplay (the scream of the deer) something we associate with a familiar mechanic, as a reward and connotation of control, and by turning that into something that is now *out* of our control – we introduce this element of uncertainty and doubt for the player. It is therefore up to the player to now interpret what this means and *what to do next*. The character in the game may also offer some interpretative visions as to what this sound is, perhaps via some sparse dialogue spoken softly and breathily to themselves. This would either be the character trying to be logical, to reassure themselves about what the sound means, or as the situation continues and becomes stranger, they can start to question themselves and unravel a little from a psychological point of view, perhaps even shouting out something – to the unseen hunter – to attempt to regain the psychological upper-hand of this ambiguous sound game.

We could even take these kinds of ambiguous sounds further in terms of character psychology. Perhaps we discover early on in the story that the character is trying to find their child who went missing during the apocalyptic event, we could add in a few sounds, just on the edge of perception, of a child laughing or crying in the far distance. The sound would never become 100% clear that it was a child, or even *your* character's child, but it could hint through sound at a very strong driving anxiety behind the character's journey, and the real motivation and reason behind the story – these kind of subtle sounds could play at certain times in the game, in highly stressful moments, or quiet moments, for example when the sun is setting and the light begins to fade low enough that hunting and navigation becomes more challenging – another indicator that we are entering a world dominated by sound, not light, and that we are entering deeper into a more frightening and psychological inner world at night.

The night especially, or any moment of darkness, is a fantastic opportunity in which to push the psychological or emotional elements of environmental sound design precisely because we forego most of the reassuring concrete reality that we see with our eyes. In low light, we are only capable of *interpreting* what we hear, rather than validating the causes of sounds with the visual. And it is through that interpretive mechanism, that we are trying to figure out if we recognise the sound, and where it is. The problem with sound only is, (for characters in dark rooms, rather than a problem for sound designers) that it does not give the brain a definitive, single objective image... it gives the brain something that could represent different things to different people. Something moving in the rubble in the *same* room, in low or no light, can have the same frightening misinterpretation and ambiguity as a distant sound – though it can be considered a more serious threat, because it is in the *same* room.

Some games use this in extreme ways by having a single light source available to the player, for example a flashlight. By allowing the player to only clearly see a narrow focussed beam of light in the direction in which they are pointing, the developers are increasing the radius of this black, psychological sound zone all around the player, except for wherever their tiny beam of light shines. So, hearing some rocks or rubble move to the right, we instantly, as players, will want to check to see what that movement is. It may be revealed to be a rat or mouse moving around. After a few of these moments becoming established, we no longer feel the need to pay attention to those minor movement sounds, and thus introduce the opportunity for a pattern breaker. By not seeing the source of sounds in the immediate diegesis, we become even more anxious, because whatever is making those sounds is close to us, and always close enough to touch us. Perhaps whatever it is can sense and *see us* very clearly, and we are at a disadvantage in *their* environment. This idea of contracting and expanding what is outside of our vision is a very powerful one and can be done not just with low or no light, but equally with fog, smoke, or dense environments like thick foliage, or even low visibility underwater environments.

By lowering visibility and readability in each of the diegetic bands, we can increase the amount of ambiguity at play in the immediate diegesis, and therefore heighten the psychological design and impact of sound much closer to the player. Of course, we can still use distant diegetic events as psychological sounds, but in darkness we can now also activate close sounds in this same manner for even more powerful dramatic effect.

Ambiguity in the ethereal diegesis

Radio dialogue is often obfuscated in this same psychological way by the simple device of having the radio or telephone voice break up and be interrupted by static. The effect is that what was previously an established reliable connection to another human being, a connection to information and reassurance, is now being taken away and made unreliable. Half-hearing words may mean that our character misinterprets critical information and therefore

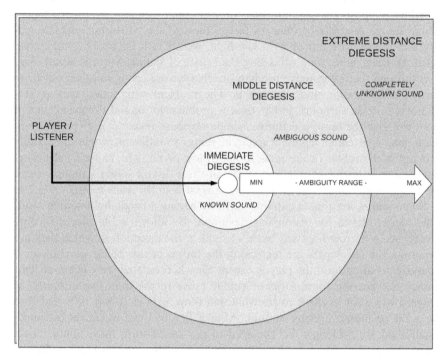

Figure 12.1 Extreme distance with reduced visibility and ambiguity range

makes the wrong decision, or feels anxious because they missed some critical information, or that their companion on the other end of the radio may even be in trouble. Half-hearing scrambled voices or conversation on the radio, now out of context, invites misinterpretations. Similarly, eavesdropping on radio conversations and inferring a different meaning because you missed the first contextual part of what was being said, can lead to exposing psychological needs, flaws and desires in our characters.

Emotional environments and the tides of ambiguity

By allowing the player more room to interpret the sub-texts of a story, and the more subtle sub-threads on narrative ideas to express themselves in addition or opposition to what is concretely seen onscreen, we can build in emotional depth that can be explored by the player both environmentally in 3D, and also emotionally through the characters. By doing this we create a kind of 3D emotional environment, which can be explored and interpreted through the lenses of character and story. So, when thinking about the sound design, it is important to consider not only what would appropriately be a heard in reality in those environments, but what the *emotional interpretation* of sounds in the environment through a character would be. The hybrid of environmental and emotional sound is useful because through this we are able to establish a subjective reality, a particular point of view, and one which can influence greatly our sound design. I often like to think about the idea of what we cannot immediately see, as the element of psychological sound that can convey more of the sub-text of the game's story – without necessarily resorting to music. This ambiguity is also very much like a tide that can be dynamically managed through the game's environmental direction and that can increase, and decrease, based on the amount of tension needed at any time. It is something that could certainly be mapped out and designed in quite a detailed way. Like everything else in games, this is also something that requires a great deal of collaboration and co-ordination between departments – sound cannot simply take the reins and run with this without the team – this requires a healthy collaborative spirit in order to facilitate a co-ordinated interplay between visuals and sounds, handing over from one to the other. Mapping out player experience at this psychological level is an area where sound can lead and where listening can take the spotlight in terms of the game experience. Finding and exploring these kinds of opportunities in your game's environment, story or design mechanics should always be something you are ready to explore and develop. The idea of leading with sound is every bit about *demonstrating* how sound can lead the experience of the player onscreen, and this tidal ebb and flow of ambiguity, through exploration of environments where visibility is established and then taken away, is a perfect example of where sound and visuals are working together in a co-ordinated dance for the audience. This approach requires that the sound department understand as much as they possibly can about the game, the story, what the characters are feeling and the visual world in which the game takes place.

We have been exploring ideas with almost no consideration or mention of technology, but the fact is that all the technical and implementational considerations and tools required for making your game will need to be aligned and prioritised in such a way that *supports* your ideas – whether that is through Real-Time-Parameter-Control (RTPC) values, switches or states that have been set up to express some of these concepts, like visibility, which can dynamically (state) or subtly (RTPC curve) alter the filtering or attenuation (sound over distance) of events as those values increase or decrease. Or perhaps it is at the game design and game system level, where these concepts and ideas are expressed and are represented deeper in the code of the game itself. Finding where sound ideas can lead, and where sound can fall back and follow what is onscreen, are pivotal areas in any successful approach to audio in video games – being able to articulate, express and then finally *execute* those moments is the only way to get those experiences to be enjoyed by an audience.

Notes

1 Street 2019, pp. 8–14.
2 The terms character and player are used interchangeably throughout this book because in most 3rd person perspective games, where the character is visible on screen, the player's identity or point-of-view is placed on that character onscreen – it is the character we see on screen through which we hear the sound in the game, we listen through their ears to the environment, and the sounds that are mixed to be the most important, are the ones that this fictional character prioritizes. The player, therefore in the case of 3rd person games, is enacting and experiencing the role of a character on-screen with whom it should be fairly easy to identify with in a very similar way to how we identify with characters on screen in TV shows of movies. In the case of a first-person game, however, a player is less likely to identify with the point-of-view of a character but is imagining putting themselves into the situation and worlds being depicted. So, their own point-of-view, their own emotions, and their own experience is to the fore-front, with no character on screen with which they can identify, they have the freedom to imagine themselves in the experience. The term 'player character' is an interesting one to consider here too, as it implies that the player is the character, and I think the term works well across both 3rd person and first-person perceptive video games. So the character, is by extension a reference to the player, as controller of that character - but just as equally, for the audience of video games who do not play, but who spectate either live or through YouTube videos of video games, are able to identify with the characters depicted on screen in a 3rd person game, and, interestingly, when watching and spectating a first person video game, to identify with the other player who is recording or streaming the footage.

13 Sound design

Designing for three audiences (player, spectator, creator)

Understanding your audience, who they are and what they receive from sound, is an area in game development that is under-discussed, yet is a critical element in being able to do things with the sound design of your game where the audience is given the right information and emotion that they need to understand the game. If the sound in a game is confusing (beyond managed and designed ambiguities as previously discussed) in terms of not being able to read what is happening, or not receiving satisfactory clear feedback when actions are completed well, or poorly, the player will be confused and irritated. Through sound, a player can receive just the right kind of emotionally shaped information, delivered at the right time, in order to remain immersed and engaged in the experience. All sound design is, to some extent, the crafting of information in an emotional wrapper.

This is also where we need to diverge from the assumption that the audience for your game is simply 'a player' who only cares about information. The element of the audience that is 'playing' the game can theoretically be separated from the part that is aesthetically enjoying the experience, in fact, the audience for games is increasingly likely to not be *a player* at all. The majority of people who experience your game may now be mainly in the category of *spectator*. Similarly, an increasingly large amount of people who experience your game may be co-creators, using in-game tools to re-author brand new content inside the universe and rules of your game world or game ecosystem as in the case of 'Roblox', or Sony's 'Dreams'. So, we will consider these three audiences for games, and look a little closer at how the sound design may need to be layered, in order for each of those audiences to be accommodated.

Audience 1: player

Understanding the player's need for information from the game is one of the more established areas of game sound design, because it is the primary layer where all game sound design begins.

The player, depending on the game, is first and foremost expecting information and feedback, information on what potential threats exist, and where they are located – what their character's health situation is, what nearby resources they have access to, what is nearby in the environment that is a potential threat or a resource and also what the next waypoint or objective is. In design terms, this primary informational feedback layer and functionality (including decisions about audibility in the mix) needs to be satisfied first, this can be thought of as the *survival* layer of information.

So, when we are attempting to build up the sound for any part of a game, we are often (though never exclusively) approaching the design with these needs in mind first.

Often this information is a confirmation of an action that they have chosen. An easy to illustrate example is in user-interface sound design, where we are creating sound to match and re-enforce navigation and selection in a menu of options. Hearing a click, or similar, sound while navigating around a menu is reassuring and offers a physical result (air moves that can be heard through the ears) from the navigation event – more pertinently when selecting an option, and confirming that option, a positive sound for affirmation, and a neutral sound for cancelling or backing out of that choice. All this can be delivered in an emotionally and stylistically engaging package, through sounds designed to match well with the aesthetic and tone of the game – thereby keeping the player 'in the world' wrapper of the game. Navigating a menu like this in silence can be a frustrating and uncertain experience, devoid of that confirmatory information and also devoid of any emotional background against which your actions, in the user interface, are being carried out.

Other examples of feedback for the player are things like firing a weapon and hitting an enemy target. It is often a requirement from the design of the game's shooting mechanics that when a weapon is fired at an enemy, and *hits* that target, that some kind of impact feedback sound should play to *confirm* to the player that they have been successful – though this sound may not be anything that could be heard in reality, other than from the perspective of the enemy being hit, it is still something that has value in the sound *design* of the game. Once this feedback through sound is established in terms of affirmatory meaning, it becomes an important part of the internal logic and rule system of the game in question. 3D proximity of enemy, or NPC, footsteps may also be a very useful part of a game's feedback system to pass information to the player about the location of other characters in the scene and their relative positions. This kind of information, not just the position, but the precise position, can be passed to the player through playback of this recognisable sound *from* the enemy's position in 3D space. The degree to which precision is a factor can be taken as far as is deemed important for the game, either very precise object-based spatial panning, or a more vague sense of position, with some spread in the 3D sphere, in the latter case, perhaps because the enemy or source of the sound is large and loud (like a T-Rex).

The design of sound from this informational and feedback perspective is often the very first 'layer' of sound that is worked on by a sound designer.

This can be referred back to our L1 level of sound design where the quality, style and identity of the sound (the emotional part) is not yet necessary to consider in the design, but the feedback and playback of the sound at the right time, in the right sequence, connected to the right game trigger in the correct way, is the most important foundational element upon which to build to the next step...

Audience 2: spectator

Another audience, and a secondary concern, or layer, of our audience are *spectators*. This could be the player when they are less involved in action or combat, and are sat back to engage with story elements of cut-scenes or conversations, or it could be the person who is sat next to the player, in the same room, who is participating in the experience as though they were the passenger on in a car on a journey, observing, engaging with the characters and story, but not *driving* the character on screen. There are also more people watching video games being played than ever before thanks to live streaming and this secondary audience is one that doesn't *need* all the information and feedback from the game that the player does, as they are involved in watching the game being played as a narrative and contextual experience. A significant audio factor here is whether the streamer is narrating the experience as they play it, or if the game is being presented entirely without commentary.

In terms of making and crafting sounds, considering the narrative and emotional perspective is something that is usually something we think about and attend to with our second pass of sound design that is applied after our initial 'player feedback' pass – basically our L2 and even further polished with the L3 pass. A lot of time can be spent on iteration here, just as it is in heavily narrative driven experiences like 'The Last of Us', that can just as easily be watched and enjoyed as a movie-like experience, as much as they are 'played' by a player. This aesthetics-centred pass will translate to the narrative expectations of a spectator audience very well. Interestingly, any annoyingly repetitive sounds, or sounds that are extremely loud in the mix due to gameplay importance, could be overlooked by a *player,* who is engaged in the experience from more mechanical and performative sense – but these sounds will become intensely annoying to a spectator audience who is not interested in the information that these sounds provide the player.

Audience 3: creator

A third audience is that of the creator. This audience is one who is using a game's content building features (in the case of both Little Big Planet or Planet Coaster) or an in game editor (in the case of Minecraft's Creative Mode or Roblox) to place and edit elements in a level – or even an entirely separate editor (as used by Roblox) to create their own content for a game – which can then be shared with players online in the game's ecosystem. These kinds of games must deliver complex systems of sounds that can handle anything that a content creator builds in their own creations, a huge challenge if you always want the game to sound great, but you do not know what the creator will do in terms of adding multiples of sound emitting objects. The *act* of creating in the engine, is also subject to much of the same feedback sound design elements as the UI sound examples that I gave earlier, given that much of their experience of *creating* is UI driven – with sound re-enforcement for things like navigation, rotation, scaling and selection. Creators also have a need to audition and hear sounds attached to objects they have placed and added in real-time, and which they can adjust and move around to better fit their creative designs. Beyond this, to help the creator's mind-set, there may also be the inclusion of ambient background sound design elements, or semi musical background moods that accompany the creation of levels, as in Planet Coaster's beautiful ambient music design which accompanies the creation process of making your own theme park.

In many of these types of games, the act of creating and making content in an editor, can be considered *the* major element of the game itself – and to this end, the design thinking behind the suite of tools provided for player/creators is almost always considered from the perspective that it should be as pleasurable and rewarding to create as it is to play.

A layered sound design approach for different audiences

This layered approach then, is one that encourages the sound designer to consider, understand and prioritise the various audiences for the game, at various times in production by separating the work into these layers, which we can approach one by one, from foundational to decorative. With this layered approach we can also avoid becoming overwhelmed by having to consider all the possible audience needs at the same time in our designs. Building in layers allows a primary foundational feedback and informational element of the sound to be devised, *then* the narrative and contextual *emotional* elements can be added to those same sounds for the spectator. Finally, the accommodation of sound settings and options, as well as culling systems for any user generated content may be considered as a final layer to affect the overall propagation of the sound being output by the game engine – as well as an additional layer of rich, UI experience for any content creation mode that is planned for the title.

Of course, understanding your audiences for the game can go into further detail in terms of user research and looking more specifically at the tastes and expectations of players who are the most likely to play your particular title – this research will also give you more relevant pointers as to what other media your specific audience demographic is likely to engage with, such as movies, or music, which can influence your approaches for each layer of sound design.

By way of a summary for this chapter there are two important takeaways. The first is that the audience for games, the people we are making and designing the experience *for*, are many and varied. These can be broken down into three strata of players, spectators and creators.

The second is that the nomenclature of talking about who we make games for needs to be updated to accommodate these three (or more) audiences when we are *developing* sound for games. As developers, we all too often converse exclusively about the player, but we need to redefine the people we make games for as 'the audience'.[1] 'The audience' is an inclusive term I use to recognise and include players, spectators, creators, as well as any additional audiences that may become prominent in engaging with the experiences being made in the future.

Note

1 In cinema, the 'audience' is fragmented between two main arenas, firstly the movie-theatre-going public who experience the film in a movie-theatre, a space that has an established cultural set of behavioural expectations built around how to best receive the experience (generally in quiet (though not in some cultures around the world), dark, but shared with others) – as well as the secondary audience of home entertainment – whether that is through playback from a disc, or streamed – the reception and dynamics of the home environment are extremely different and have a wider range of dynamic possibilities (perhaps your home is quiet, perhaps it is chaotic) perhaps you have good home theatre sound, or average to poor TV speaker sound. Either way, audio is quite often tailored to have two mixes for these different audiences (a theatrical mix and a home theatre mix).

14 Sound playback dynamics

Thinking horizontally, vertically and diagonally about asset design

A very important creative and communicative tool for us to be able to make clear decisions, collaborate with the rest of the inter-disciplinary team and allow us to lead the process of creative development with sound, is to understand, develop and make use of *intensity curves*.

Being able to work directly with other disciplines, such as art, narrative and the game direction itself, often represents a challenge in terms of communication – different terminology, tools, pipelines and dependencies. However, finding a gathering point where all disciplines can come together and discuss the experience is immeasurably valuable. Standing together as a team in front of an intensity curve which *visualises* the experience everyone is working on, kind of like a graphical music score, allows many opportunities to clarify and discuss information about the overall dynamics and tension of the experience being created for the audience. Each member of the team looks at the curve through their disciplinary lenses yet can also talk about all the other disciplinary lenses at the same time.

To visualise this even further, we can even plot discipline-specific curves, around a central spinal curve of the overall experience.

Sometimes called a dynamics curve, intensity curve or tension curve, this graphic sets out to visualise the intensity of the experience over time. It usually tracks in time by using major 'beats' within whatever section is being depicted – whether that is a gameplay feature, a cinematic scene, or an entire narrative segment, mission or map – there is always an overall dramatic shape to the experience and getting it on paper is a huge step for inter-disciplinary collaboration. From this will spring a common point of reference, where all disciplines have some simple way for co-ordinating their work. The tension curve allows us to do this in an easy to understand, interpretative, visual manner.

In figure 14.1, we can see an example tension curve for a cinematic scene in a game…

This is just one example scene; it is at the very beginning of the game and is used to establish the tone excitement and the action right up front for the audience.

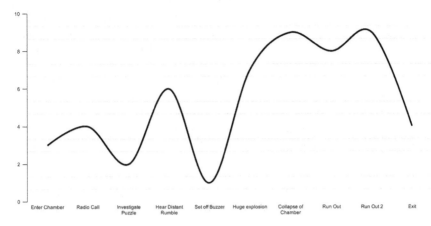

Figure 14.1 Cinematic tension curve

There are a few ways to look at and talk about this kind of tension curve. The first is to understand the overall shape and get a sense of where the more extreme moments of stillness are, as well as the extreme moments of intensity. We can perhaps ask which is the *most intense* moment and how do we get there and set that up?

The second way to read this is to look at the difference between neighbouring points. For example, the difference between the moment just before, and the highest intensity moment is a difference of 8 units ('set off buzzer' and then 'huge explosion'). This is a huge sudden change in intensity over a relatively short amount of time. For the player this will be felt far more acutely than the difference between the first two moments ('intro' and 'enter chamber'), where we have a very subtle *decrease* of intensity from 5 to 3, a difference of only 2 intensity units.

We can see that before we reach any kind of intensity peak, and there are a few of those, we often have a reduction in the intensity just before. This reduction exists in order to make sure there is a contrast, thus making the difference feel more extreme and intense. The bigger that contrast is, the wider that gap, the higher the difference in intensity will feel for the audience.

These *contrasts* are very important in terms of making things feel dynamic and dramatic onscreen and are essential in engaging an audience. A curve that is constantly moving and has a lot of extremes could be described as more of a roller coaster experience, whereas an experience that has subtle change over time, perhaps building slowly to a single moment would be a more intimate experience that can take place over a longer period of time.

One thing that should generally be avoided in any kind of experience is any flat curve, where the intensity or tension continues at the same number or changes very little over two or three beats. If you see any two moments that have the same intensity value, you are looking at a flat experience and this should raise some flags and stimulate some conversations about the audience experience, and about what can be done in order to differentiate those moments in terms of intensity.

Once you have plotted out an intensity curve (sometimes this is the role of the creative director, though in lieu of having these from a creative director they can be authored by the audio director (or anyone else) and approved by the creative director) the next step would be to discuss the curve with the rest of the team, ideally with someone who represents the overall high-level creative vision from each discipline. They certainly may see or raise points with perhaps some of the numbers for the overall curve, they may offer suggestions as to how to tweak or better represent certain beats within the overall curve. Ideally, we suggest adding their own discipline-specific intensity curve to the diagram, for example to show *lighting*.

Audio specific curves

The further step of elaborating on intensity curves, once you have an approved and agreed upon overall shape to the main curve, is to take the idea now into a single discipline direction – in this case for audio in general. This allows us to really dig into the specific food-groups of audio in the game at every particular beat. The wonderful thing about this is that we now have a way of reviewing the context for every food-group in the game, and we can evaluate and talk about how certain groups may change over time in relation to the curve. This is probably one of the most useful tools for leading a sound team (and a game team) in terms of having a coherent map of how the game experience will feel for an audience.

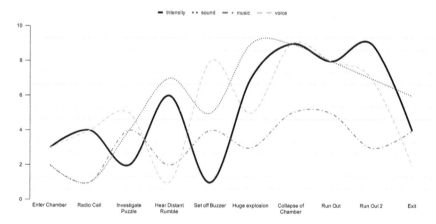

Figure 14.2 Audio specific tension curve

In this example we still plot the overall intensity, but we now introduce three new curves to support it, one of which represents the music, one the sound and the other the voice.

Each line plots the intensity of each food-group and breaking into these separate streams can be useful when thinking about clarity in the mix, especially in determining and illustrating where are the intense music moments, the voice moments and the sound moments in a mix. If a music curve falls to 0 on the graph, then we can understand that the score is no longer present at this moment. If voice is around 1 or 2 on the graph, then we can assume that only sparse dialogue, or ambient background conversations from NPCs is present, contrasted with a 10, which would show the most intense shouting and screaming of a central character.

It is also important to understand that though these visualised curves can allow us to be more precise than we would be with just words, they remain very interpretive in nature, and will require the person who authored the curve (the director, or the lead) to be available to explain and answer questions about the curve, and what each moment represents.

In this sense, another additional element to build into this audio-specific version of the curve is a section of sound notes for each beat discipline. When I am doing this, I like to mention themes, perhaps adjectives and conjure, through a short description, some of the poetry and inspiration of the experience from the audience's perspective, how the characters and audience should feel. These additional notes can also provide more detail and more interpretation for the rest of the sound team, so that they may be able to better implement the vision for the scene.

The more this is discussed with the team, and the more the vision of this dynamics curve is implemented onscreen, almost certainly the intensity curve visuals will need to be updated. This is perfectly normal, as long as the curve is kept up to date with the latest state of the game onscreen, then the information is still extremely useful and relevant – right up to the final master mix stage of the game.[1]

Intensity curves: who and when

I strongly encourage the audio director, or lead, to volunteer to be responsible for producing and organising cross discipline discussion around intensity curves, and even the creation of the curve documents themselves. These curves are extremely useful touchstones for anyone in the team to come together and start to understand the high-level vision of a scene or gameplay feature, cinematic or map. But in the process of having to make them, you will need to learn everything you can about the game in order to create the curves. The production of these curves does not need to occur *before* the work is started, there usually comes a particular moment in the production of a dramatic piece of work, when this kind of graph becomes necessary in mid-production – the script may have already been written, or the overall beats may have already been laid out and roughly implemented. I would expect (going back to our 'L level' description) that during the end of L2 phase and before the beginning of the L3 phase, the curves would ideally be available for the team and starting to be discussed in order to get the sound, *and game*, to a more polished and dynamic L3 state. The more that people in the different disciplines have an overall idea about the dynamic shape of the game, the easier it will be to communicate and discuss this though such a graph. It will also come in extremely useful for pushing the mix and the separation and subsequent coordination of each food-group in the L3 stage.

This contextualisation of sounds on a timeline across beats brings us to thinking about sound asset design out of isolation, and into the idea of a continually changing context. Interactive sound in games needs to be considered quite deeply in three contextually driven ways, vertically, horizontally and diagonally.

Vertical asset design (micro-variations)

Thinking about the *verticality* of a sound's requirements is an acknowledgement of how often the sound event is expected to trigger over time in the game. If a sound is going to be re-triggered a lot, it will require a high degree of *variation* in order to help it not feel mechanical, repetitive and annoying. This is a form of micro dynamics that helps the human ear (and really the brain) to believe that there are small differences. Similar to the way we hear small variances in the real world when repeating an action, these slight variations occur based on all kinds of factors like temperature, weight, surface variation, impulse strength and so on. Footsteps, gunshots, body falls or punch impacts, the things that games allow you, as a player, to do repeatedly when you continually press and repress an action button, are often the areas that need the most attention in terms of these micro-variations. This kind of sound design and thinking about sound, expresses the *micro stories* that we are telling about these sounds. I think of this as vertical, because it is like a large vertical stack of sound variations that can be randomized each time the same event is triggered.

Horizontal asset design (micro narratives)

The approach that considers the variation of sounds over time is referred to as horizontal asset design. When thinking about the sound design of an object, or something that is going to be heard through the game beyond just a single static interaction in a single static location, we need to consider how that sound will be affected and changed, in terms of the life of that sound over time, this is like the micro-narrative of that sound. This is typically a much longer-term narrative variation across a story than the short micro-variations mentioned in the vertical asset design. Horizontal variation can take into account the first time you use something, and the amount of development that will occur with that object in terms of sound, over time to signify those changes. The first time you use a specific magical spell we could want that to feel fairly low in power, but as you develop skills and knowledge in the game, the same spell could build into something extremely powerful –- it should still have many of the same sound ingredients and identity, but it will have a horizontal design element over time that enables it to build and feel more powerful.

The shifting design and context of these sounds *over time*, while not changing the *broad* design direction and sound character of the weapon or spell over time, does change the lens through which we hear it, and brings some additional considerations to the design over time and within different contexts – this is the horizontal approach. As well as variation, we also consider *consistency* of certain broad sound elements, such as helicopters, weapons and so on, sounds that may be under the ownership of a single designer for the entirety of the project. Achieving this consistency (*horizontal consistency*) is a primary requirement of design for horizontal sound elements in a game, but the secondary design layer should be some kind of contextualisation depending on what lens the sound is being heard through at any particular time (*horizontal variation*). This may be subtle, like a slight push and pull of EQ or volume over the time of the game – or it may be an additional layer added or removed at various times to exaggerate a feeling of power or weakness as required.

Combined approach: diagonal asset design

When the two elements of micro variations and micro narratives are considered together, this holistic approach is known as a complete *diagonal asset design* approach. It is the ideal that games would strive for when they are considering the feedback that is given to the player from dynamic sound design. This approach will certainly require the deepest level of collaboration of a few different sound designers, such as generalists who may be responsible for particular maps, and also a specialist sound designer who may be responsible only for a few of the horizontal elements like vehicles, ambiences, Foley or weapons.

Given the importance of both understanding the dynamics curves that are expressed and validated by the team, and the experience of the audience, there is a need to have a renewed focus on the moment to moment adjustments of sound that takes into account dynamic context.

Note

1 If you have plotted the intensity curves for the entire game, this would be an incredibly useful document with which to begin discussions about the final mix with a re-recording mixer who is perhaps new to the project at the L4 stage of sound development. However, and I will discuss this in more detail in the mixing section of the book, at the stage of the project when you are thinking about the overall experience with a re-recording mixer, you must also be prepared to let these pieces of paper and documents go, in order to work with the more organic and real material of the overall mix of the entire game onscreen.

15 Designing a moment

Temporality in interactive sound design

Given that we have now established how important it is to develop intensity curves (dynamic change cover time), we can start to build deeper detail into the changing context of sound from one moment to the next in the game. Understanding a sound's evolving context is extremely important because it will tell you, the sound designer, what the emotional and gameplay lenses are that you are looking through – the importance of foreshadowing the next event or beat, the important of letting the player know they are running low on a particular resource, be that health, ammunition, or oxygen if underwater – sounds can and should change over time given the different contexts the player finds themselves in. Sound designers are, and should always be, context junkies, because understanding context is the only method through which we will be able to express the correct information and feeling to the audience as well as understanding the overall interactive design range of the sound, and how it needs to change over time and circumstance.

It is important to understand not just the moment you are designing, but the *entire context* that this moment occupies within the continuum of the rest of the gameplay, or story in regard to the sounds being used. What is the moment preceding? What is the moment following? Getting the right information for these contexts can be tricky in game development, because the development process is so fluid, ongoing and iterative, and even contextual itself among different disciplines. Unfortunately, the overall *web of contexts* can sometimes only be revealed and apparent to those making the game, towards the end of the development.

Designing an explosion sound can take an almost infinite amount of forms and depending on what happened previously in the recent memory of the player, the explosion may need to accomplish different things beyond just an 'epic explosion' which is seen onscreen.

Let's take an example. (*In this example the explosion signifies a wall that has been brought down by one of our team mates so that we can get through and escape from an enclosed compound – once we hear the comms and then the explosion occurs, we must move fast, as the private security team will no doubt be alerted and come straight into action to find us and respond.*) From a gameplay viewpoint, our explosion needs to be clearly audible and communicate to the player that the explosion has occurred, while also relaying the 3D location to the player so that they know in which direction to proceed to escape. Because of its gameplay and narrative importance, we really need to hear this explosion, as well as quite a long tail to keep its 3D location present for longer. We also need it to play really big, because it is an explosion big enough to punch a hole in a thick perimeter wall of a compound. It also needs to be louder and more significant than other gameplay explosion sounds, in order to sound more significant – I should say that all around us many explosions are playing from mortar rockets and grenades, as the private security team (bad guys) try to find us. Moving on to some of the other sounds that occur *around* the explosion, we can do several things to make more room for this moment: we can *precede* the moments prior with some stillness and moments of tension – almost all of this will need to be co-ordinated with the design and scripting team, so we can stop mortar and grenade launching events occurring a few seconds before our main explosion occurs. In that same preceding moment, we can also begin to de-emphasise (duck down) other ambient sounds that are playing, like dripping water on leaves and anything that the player may be otherwise hearing in the immediate visual area, this allows the player to use their hearing to 'reach' further into the outer diegesis where the explosion is expected to happen. Now we are getting into the storytelling contexts: we now suddenly hear a few distant shouts of an enemy guard as they discover our team mate, then we hear a few gunshots, from their location – an immediate cause for concern as this would mean that our team mate has been discovered, and also that they may or may not have been able to set off the explosion – some more shouts from an enemy security guard to alert the others – all the while we retain our position and still wait for the cue – the anxiety building all the time. Then when the explosion is finally triggered, something feels wrong... the explosion goes off early with no warning, and we receive no comms telling us that the explosion will be triggered as arranged. Our teammate was discovered and had to set off the explosion early, in the process killing the guard who discovered them, as well as seriously injuring themselves. We hear the news from our injured teammate over the radio. Knowing a particular sequence of events is going to occur, but then having that go wrong, as sound designers the explosion can be designed through this lens using adjectives such as 'premature, unexpected' (we can interpret this as having a very sudden transient at the beginning of the sound, almost like receiving a sudden shock) 'sickening', 'revealing' (we can interpret this as having a long, low tail to the sound, the sound that was supposed to signal our escape from this mission, is now exposed and audible to everyone in the complex, the sound going on for longer than would be naturally expected keeps it alive in both our own ears and the ears of the enemy, meaning everyone can hear this and will now be headed towards that location). Hearing the echoes of the sound around the entire, wider environment can also help achieve this affect. Then, even before the tail of the sound has decayed away, we can begin to hear the alarms and sounds and shouts of activity from the security team as they begin to respond. As a player, this will induce a panic and a need to confront them as they get between our location and that of the hole in the perimeter wall, and our inured teammate. So, the time pressure is on. Hearing alarms and the distant scurrying of the enemy all around us, including some occasional distant shots, raises the player's attention and awareness of sounds around them. All this is occurring offscreen, so we are relying on our ears to communicate the story of what is happening. We had a plan, we had expectations of what to listen for, and those expectations started to unravel and change through sound.

Back to the sound designer's perspective, for this example, on paper, if we simply received a list of sound effects to design from the design department, without context, such as 'wall explosion', 'distant gun shots', 'enemy walla shouting' (not dialogue lines, as it would be indeterminate as to what was said) and 'distant alarms' we would not be able to put the story of those sounds together. Without understanding the narrative, the sequences of events, and the expectations of what the player is listening for – we would just assemble this scene perhaps using our *own* interpretation on what the most important sounds were, and how they are heard. If we just get this informa-tion in the form of a shopping list of sound effects to give to the sound team to just create those assets as listed, working to simply check those things off a list, we would lose all this important contextual detail. The first question the sound designer is hopefully going to ask, about each and every one of those sounds, is what the context is, what is happening before and after each sound in the scene. What is expected outcome, vs the surprise of this outcome we hear, and in what sequence are these sounds occurring? It may seem hard to believe that sound design can be commissioned without knowing these things, but it happens *all the time.*

Sound may go even further in creating a narrative *sound story* in this example, by deciding to exaggerate even more tension and feeling that something is wrong. In the moments before we hear the explosion, we may decide to create some ominous portents in the immediate diegesis where the player is situated – bringing down insect sounds around the player (insects would normally not be affected by anything other than the temperature of the environment or close proximity of a predator) could be a subtle hint to the player that something is wrong, a sign, an omen. Adding some confusing and ambiguous sounds in the extreme distant diegesis may similarly add tension to the stillness prior to the explosion, perhaps a distant 1980s telephone ringer from another house way up on a hill, filtered through the environment, echoing and reverberated, this would certainly add an element of intrigue, and it would add an expected and unpre-dictable image to the general feeling – very distant and very subtle, these slight and unexpected sounds can start to bring in this idea of unpredictability and we can start to feel that our character's plan is unravelling. This kind of orchestra-tion of sounds in the diegesis, particularly ambiguous sounds, brings all kinds of questions and feeling to the player – especially heightened in a situation where the player is already focussed and listening out for specific cues from the teammate. Adding additional sound stories does not always require tight integration between the audio and design scripting teams, we are exploiting an already created lull in the action and adding something in there to create further tension and further our contexts. As long as we don't place sounds that ruin or distract attention too much from the overall idea.

Much of building the context around sound requires that this kind of cross-discipline orchestration and knowledge transfer needs to take place – it is orchestration not only of the sounds themselves, and the timing and location at which those sounds occur, but also the co-ordination of, and *separation of,* the triggers for those sounds. This can require a lot of meetings and conversation in front of white boards, or in front of the game itself, understanding visually and temporally what is happening in the scene and where. Once the details of the scene are understood across the teams, the design elements of the sound may require an even further level of planning and detail into exploring the unseen and in-between areas of the scene, the moments where a sound is triggered, but may need a lot more time and space than was originally thought from the L1 version. Sometimes event sequencing and tuning requires a few milliseconds, sometimes seconds. Co-ordinating the temporal fabric of an in-game moment and its triggering events can be quite complex, but it is all achievable with a good team who can communicate fluidly across disciplines, having the right level of detailed conversations, and the right reviews at the right time. It is essential to have representatives of all the disciplines at such a review – staying on the same page can be difficult within game development teams, and it is easy for one discipline to understand the scene from one context or perspective, whereas another discipline sees and interprets the scene from an entirely different perspective. All these differences, in this web of contexts, should be confronted and reconciled as soon as possible, and the only way to do that is through review and conversation about context, and again, always coming back to asking what is the most important thing in the scene.

Getting to the most important thing could be a question like 'what is the most important thing for this character at this moment' – meaning their motivation, what are they listening for – or it could be 'what is the most important thing for the *player* at this moment'. There is often a narrative subtext priority – for example, hearing the location via audible cues, of the person you are supposed to be rescuing, combined with a simultaneous *gameplay* priority, for example low health. The narrative priority is often overtaken by the gameplay priority, pushing the narrative elements into the background, but not removing them entirely. Narrative tells us the immediate and overall emotional goal, whereas the gameplay priority is giving us the immediate survival needs on a second-to-second basis.

The creation of a tension curve is a good starting point to understanding the dynamics and priorities of the various elements that go into making up a game – these can be created for gameplay areas such as combat, or exploration, or traversal experiences, but they can also be created for maps overall, as well as cinematic scenes as we have highlighted. They allow teams to come together to talk about and think about what the experience is that they are creating for the player. They are a focal point for developers to plot the journey that the player will be taken on, and to figure out where the dynamics of the game are at a given moment. From here, the team can begin to really dive in and talk about the detail of the smaller contexts of those scenes. A single plot on a dynamics curve may be zoomed-into and exploded to reveal several smaller sub curves or sub events that are driving the overall intensity of that particular moment, all the while understanding more about the context of each moment, and of the needs of each sound. Once this information is understood, then the actual work of designing and implementing those sounds, can begin – and from there, through regular reviews and meetings, the work can be tweaked adjusted and polished until the desired experience at the desired quality level is reached.

16 Leading with sound

Spectacle and immersion

Even before implementing sound in the game engine, we can quickly sketch a sense of what the game, or game feature, may sound and feel like for an audience. This kind of sketching can be validated early on by the creative team, and used as a guide, both emotionally and tonally for the rest of the team in implementation.

Much of communicating the sound style to the wider development team, as well as exposing the world of sound creation processes and techniques to the team, can be considered as a spectacle within itself, and it is this spectacle that can be used to great effect to showcase sound and illuminate some of the invisible work that is being done on a daily basis with sound.

Having video footage of recording sessions, whether that is studio based Foley, or trips to outside locations – field recording footage for special effects sources is great, but very common – and going even further beyond capturing the source material, to exposing the wider team to some of the *creative spectacle* of processing and implementing sound can be extremely interesting and sometimes even jaw-dropping to a general audience. Understanding that some of the magic of simple sound manipulation may have worn off on us sound designers long ago but can still be extremely enthralling for a general audience, is key. Try to see our craft through fresh eyes and ears and this will give you many ideas for what to show to the team. The most basic pitching up or down of sounds can reveal hidden worlds within recordings, illustrating and demonstrating these as part of weekly stand-ups, or monthly show and tell meetings can certainly open up the idea of working more closely with sound in mind for the team – as well as even opening up the ideas and notions that what is *invisible*, what is not seen, but what is *felt* by the player, is just as important as what is seen and rendered on screen for the audience.

These spectacles and showcases can also be curated and saved in reserve for showcasing the sound to the wider public audience for the game too. Video focuses on sound design are especially common and increasingly of interest to players and those interested in what goes into making games. Care should be taken to avoid any notion, all too common in '*making of*' sound videos, that sound is somehow a quirky, obsessive and unusual element to the production of a game, and also that the sound team are following their *own* path as auteurs, rather than that of the game team as a whole – the recording and designing of the sound effects should never become more important than the game itself. Greater emphasis on implementation, iteration processes, collaboration and contextual approaches to dynamic sound can certainly be of interest to audiences, and will also supply the optics that sound is a fully integrated part of the production process of a game.

Sound can be pushed much further in games to express emotion and point of view, especially when we consider and exaggerate areas through context and ambiguity, using sound to push the player to listen in particular interpretations of what they see and hear, encouraging the ears of the audience to reach *into* the world, much further beyond what is simply expressed already onscreen visually. By having our characters listen to and be aware of sound deeper in the worlds that we are putting onscreen, we are giving our audiences the ability to reach deeper too. Therein lies some of the magic of sound, as a gateway to wanting to be immersed, and wanting to *believe* beyond what is merely seen. As audiences, we all want to escape, briefly, from the realities of real-world problems. We have a great deal of responsibility to our audiences to give them a believable world in which to navigate, explore, immerse and express themselves. When our work is successful, the player will rarely notice the subtle and detailed work that has been done to accomplish engagement with the game world. When nothing is pulling you out of this world, then the role of sound is one of true immersion.

On this note, and to complete this section on sound, I would like to offer my three guiding principles for good sound design, inspired directly by Braun's Product Designer Dieter Rams' Ten Principles of Good Design. These are very high-level principles for game sound that, hopefully at least, never shift or move, no matter what the platform, or the genre. They can generally be applied to almost anything that you play or work on.

Good sound design is…

Simple

All elements are reduced to what is essential only. Reducing and subtracting is a continuous process that requires time. (This doesn't mean doing very little, it means iteration and refinement – removing unnecessary layers until what is left, is doing the job perfectly.)

Beautiful

The player should be enjoying the experience and be present 'in the world' emotionally, and not aware of or 'hearing' the underlying state-machines or design. (This is especially pivotal at loading times or during scene transitions – any such dead spots that reveal the technology and destroy the illusion of immersion should be a priority.)

Unique

Instantly identifiable (ideally own-able) and memorable from aesthetic standpoint. Sometimes this comes with the IP, so taking time to really understand what it is and what ideas drive it to find unique sound approaches that resonate strongly with the game's aesthetic.

Notes

1 Altman 2007. Rick Altman's book provides a thorough and fascinating account of much of the lost landscape of sound production, performance and distribution used during this period of early cinema exhibition and entertainment.
2 Sergi 2005. Gianluca Sergi's book discusses at length the concept of the super-listener.

Part III

Music

Why do we need music?

I have not studied music and don't consider myself a composer or musician. These notes on music are based entirely on my experience of editing music and working with composers in games over the past 20 years. It is often my role to communicate to the composer what the game needs from a score. But often I find equally that I am also communicating to the game what *it needs* from the music. This also puts me in the same or similar position as most of the people who are commissioning and requesting music in games, from producers to directors, but perhaps much closer in that I constantly work with the material as a music editor. In many ways I think that academic study of music can sometimes create a false sense of mastery over a subject that I believe is essentially *un-masterable*. Yes, we can break it all down into its foundational atoms and analyse the relationship between notes, as well as extrapolating and implying cultural and political contexts, but in the end, music will always resist our attempts to decode and to analyse what it is and how it works – in the end, we all experience it differently, we all experience it in the moment, and we all sense to some extent that music is ephemeral: it will soon evaporate into memory, and even our memories of music, of melodies, tones and textures will eventually fade and decay. Music can teach us much more than we think and being more open to music's influence is one of the most important things I've learned.

As a director, my approach is to work with music primarily as emotional material, an element of the game's soundtrack that is interpreting for the audience some sense of the way characters feel, even if they say and do the opposite onscreen, we can still get a sense of how they feel through the music. We use music I think because it the most direct form of empathy, of *feeling* how someone else feels. If we just wanted the audience to *know* how a character felt, we would have them say how they felt, but with music, there is an exchange of non-verbal emotional communication between the characters onscreen and the audience. Music for me can express the emotional feeling in the moment, but also allows us to hear change through that emotion over time. This is often through the development of themes and ideas, music that has a beginning and an end, and that is transformed on the way. I especially love working with this intangible material because it can bring in the release valve of ambiguity, we can interpret a scene or question what is shown to the audience, especially if a score is telling us something different to what we see.

However, music and its use, should form part of a co-ordinated approach to emotional storytelling. I believe that because music is so powerful at speaking to the audience directly, that over-reliance on it becomes a problem very quickly – overuse can rapidly diminish the power to evoke emotions.

Music can be the first thing that a creative director, or producer, will reach for, in order to add a sense of emotion and feeling to a video or element of gameplay. It is the quickest go-to crutch to prop up what is not already inherently there in the feature itself, whether that is excitement, urgency, melancholy... whatever the desired effect, music is called upon to supply the emotional element to the experience onscreen. I do this myself during very early pre-concept phases to try to understand the feeling of a project, but I am careful to rapidly develop the other audio food-groups at the same time to see how they all work together. My issue here is that it can be *entirely* left to the music to do this, when there is little to no effort to explore emotions in the other elements of the game, whether onscreen or through other food groups of sound or voice. Examples of this kind also suggests to audiences that music needs to be, and will always be, present in the overall experience. Without giving examples where music is not present, and without benchmarking how music can enter or leave a scene, we can find ourselves with a vision which champions *music all the time* – and it is almost always the case that this approach will be inherited by the game itself.

This approach can result in an end-product that is entirely driven by wall-to-wall music, with little to no emotional storytelling being allowed to develop between the other areas of sound design and voice. An approach of constant music results in an experience that wherever music is absent, it feels like a bug with the game – that the music is broken and no longer working, rather than a moment that requires no music. What tends to occur during development, is that the QA department will log any spots in the game with no music as bugs. The opposite issue can also be the case, when a music cue that is supposed to trigger, does not trigger, and the QA department do not log this as an issue because they do not know that there should be a music cue here – if nothing else, this makes the clear case for audio departments reviewing and logging these kinds of issue themselves regarding aesthetics, as well as having a full-time QA person who is involved in the daily audio briefings, so that they more fully understand whether music is needed to be present or not in specific contexts.

One of the unfortunate side-effects of reaching for music first, or too soon, is that it becomes the only element used for emotion and it becomes impossible to imagine an emotional scene or element without it. I have been guilty of this approach myself, and creatively found it hard to reverse out of the situation. The problem with this is, that music is going to end up being called on to express *every kind of emotion*, from joy to sadness to excitement to light-heartedness, and what we end up with is a soundtrack that Mickey-Mouses all over the place – the emotions of every character at every moment, laboriously telling the player what to feel at all times.

In many ways, it can be argued that music is not necessary at all to a video game's soundtrack. While I do not believe that games need to go to this extreme in order to rid themselves of the wall-to-wall approach, some kind of *reset* and a higher degree of thought, planning and understanding of music's potential and power is definitely required in games. In this focus on music, we will explore how a more considered approach can be achieved, both in co-ordination with the other elements of the sound and visual tracks, but also by understanding what music is best suited for in games, and where it best fits into a holistic approach to video game audio.

There are some examples of video games without a musical score, and these primarily seem to be on older video game systems where the lack of music was more dictated by technology limitations and financial budgets, rather than that of *design*. However, due to lack of examples of games with no music at all, we can instead look to cinema for examples of movies without scores. While art house films like Michael Haneka's 'Cache' (2005), and Thomas Vinterberg's 'Festen' (1998) have no score, some blockbuster Hollywood films like 'Back to the Future', in which the opening 15 to 20 minutes do not have a single note of musical scoring, can give us guidance. In the former two examples, the realism and sense of the everyday is emphasised through the absence of expected musical scoring, and as an audience our attention naturally shifts to reading the environmental sounds and the nuances of the dialogue performances that much more intensely. The example of 'Back to the Future' is an exceptionally good one, because in a very similar sense, absence of musical scoring is used to denote the sense of the everyday, the ordinary and the mundane, whereas, as soon as the DeLorean (time machine) makes its first appearance on screen, through musical scoring, we enter a magical otherworldly place.

Some of the most famous and often quoted examples are movies that replace those scores with evocative use of pre-written period specific licensed music. Perhaps another well-known example of this approach is '2001: A Space Odyssey', in which pre-existing music is synced and edited to the picture. The challenges of this approach are made more difficult with the interactive nature of games, in that the music needs to be edited, prepared and extended to match gameplay dynamics and give feedback to the player – all things that the original composition was never intended to do. Even with access to the stems of the original track, this would be extremely challenging and would require additional bridging material to be devised in the same style, key and tempo as the original track to make it stretch out over the new dynamic contexts of gameplay and narrative.

This is undoubtedly one of the major driving forces behind the commissioning of original musical scores in games, so that the design and system can have musical material custom made and created to integrate into those custom systems. Systems that incorporate and are designed around licensed music, like the radio stations on GTA, eradicate the need for editorial of the material and are more successful in using music as an element that mimics how we might expect to hear this kind of music in the same contexts of our everyday lives.

Of course, the option usually exists for players to be able to mute or turn down the music score in almost all games, and experience and play without the music. However, I would argue that this approach is the chosen endpoint of the player, rather than the artistically designed experience intended by the developer. One could argue that if the game were made and designed without music, then much of the sound and voice material would be approached differently to carry more of the emotive elements. Another thing worth considering is that musical scoring in games often 'hides' a lot of issues with the sound design in games, such as bad loops or poorly designed and implemented elements, which when the score is removed, can suddenly be exposed and highlighted.

17 Music as creative crutches
Reaching for music too soon and too late

As hinted at in the introduction, a great many projects reach for music almost immediately as the way that the overall soundtrack will express shape of what is occurring emotionally on screen. Very often this is a quick and easy thing to reach for in terms of sound, as it offers the opportunity to try out some already finished orchestrated or mastered music to be added to the concept work of the project. This is indeed precisely how many projects end up getting *stuck* with temp music and end up requiring a composer to match almost exactly what has been temporarily living in the project, up until it is time to replace it with composed music.

By instead using music as an element of leadership on a project, the trick is to get quickly *beyond* the temp music stages, and into the original composition phase. This may take the form of having music written, from a very high-level perspective, very early on in concept phase, to fit the overall big themes and feelings that the game is about. This would require already understanding what those big underlying themes are about and necessitate some deep conversation with the creative director. Having music created in this way, at this stage, away from the pressure to meet and match sync points of either in-game systems or cinematic scenes, has huge advantages in terms of exploring all aspects of musical material. The other great thing about writing music that poses and expresses the big, deep major themes of the project, is that they will not change or need to be updated, and that the music can explore an emotional space, and answer emotional questions, rather than being led by the ever changing visual elements of the title.

While temp music may be useful in the earliest stages of *pre-concept* – in order to quickly test mood, tone and make some initial assessments of the essence of what the project may feel like – it can very quickly become a heavy burden on the original music creation and tonal exploration processes of the game.

Partnering with a composer for the early stages of the concept phase can have enormous impact. It means the project can begin to explore the unique side of the game's moods and textures, as well as quickly removing any reliance on temp music.

As the story and game design develops in the early stages of concept, the *overall* outline of the story may be all that is known, having not yet been broken down into the acts and chapters required. A composer can still operate successfully here by scoring what *is* known, exploring overall emotion and feeling, in order to further develop the game's overall identity.

This kind of exploratory composition work, at a time when there isn't as much pressure from the production side to develop music that can be implemented into the game engine, and ensuring that it fits the needs of the design feedback and state machines for combat, exploration from the systemic standpoint, can be extremely liberating. This freedom allows exploration of the stylistic choices and orchestration, finding the voice (again, *the identity*) of the music and also of the game – without yet having to be tied and structurally influenced by the shape of the game design systems.

If a composer is brought in later, perhaps at the stage when structures and systems have been developed, this can have a huge impact on the way the music is conceived and written, as the music will also need to answer lots of very specific technical briefs and needs, rather than being asked exclusively to explore tone.

We do quite quickly arrive at a point, in most game concepts and designs, where music is thought of as an additional systemic feedback tool for the player, communicating the mechanical states of the game, usually, but not exclusively, in systemic combat situations. The systemic approach is certainly necessary in order to make video game music, and the *design* of the music, important in terms of tying together the emotion and the information for the audience. Music, just like sound, is also conveying information in an emotional wrapper. This adherence and consciousness of *design* means that the music assets need to be prepared into stems and looping segments and stingers, to match the needs of the game systems. This requires much more technical thinking about the production of the music. Of course, music composition in interactive entertainment has long taken into account and leveraged ways in which musical score can be *extended* and made to feel less-repetitive than simple short loops, through use of randomised segments, generative musical elements and stinger variations designed to be randomised or combined in unique ways, and to fit the amount of variety needed for each situation. However, this form of asset and system-*driven* music design is for the most part giving musical expression to a state machine – and requires a significant degree of the composition and execution decision making at runtime. This allows the music designer, implementers and composer to create a system of music that can theoretically continue to play over a much longer period of time than the delivered assets. This approach of fitting material to the systems doesn't help us to get around the overall problem that wall-to-wall music stops having any meaning after quite a short amount of time, even if it is designed to be *technically* non-repeating – a continual musical score presence can still *feel* repetitive and by extension, make the entire game experience feel repetitive. This effect of musical over saturation can be summarised as a feeling that the music for the game is always 'background' music rather than foreground emotional scoring. To re-iterate, partnering early on in the concept phase with a composer to work exclusively on non-systemic ideas and emotion-driven exploration, means that a musical aesthetic and language can be developed *prior* to answering the needs of any systemic music design.

I advocate an approach that is conscious that *overusing* music is effectively killing it, removing its inherent power of *highlighting* an emotional moment. Music that always plays, is always present, is emotionally the same as music that isn't there at all, and is a flat experience. We see this approach to score every movement very often in cinematics direction, where these very short sub-elements of story exposition, are expected to be fully scored in the golden-age Hollywood style, hitting every single emotional cue that is on the character's face, regardless of how the game in general is scored. Music in cinematics is almost always used as an element that *follows* the emotional requirements of the cinematics director, in much the same way that they would direct an actor. However, music has the role of telling the audience things that are not necessarily present on screen or in the script – the subtexts. If music is used in the game to provide what is *needed* emotionally in terms of subtext, then a similar approach in the cut scenes will need to be taken – cinematics should always adopt the music strategy developed in the rest of the game, never the other way around (unless, of course, you are working on a cinematics *driven* experience).

A sparser approach to scoring here is also encouraged, if the music is telling you something that is already present on screen, then it is redundant. Musical score is always at its most effective when it is telling us the *inner* story, not the external story of that we can *already* see onscreen. As an audience, we crave to understand and connect with this emotional context, what the characters feel, and this deeper element of a story, scene or feature is a line of storytelling that isn't present all that often in the visual scene.

We don't need music to do everything, to tell us absolutely everything about the game, about all its design-based state machines and convey all possible emotions *all the time*. As mentioned already, we see this excessive approach begin to take root in some early prototype work where, rather than reaching for sound design first, music is used as a proxy for the entire soundtrack. This *music everywhere* approach also leaves very little room for sound and voice to come through in the mix, regardless of how many frequency holes (a futile *technical* solution) are left in the music track for these elements to poke through. The end result sounds and feels overwhelming, with little co-ordination or dynamics, making mixing the game almost impossible. In the end, this approach results in music needing to be mixed extremely quietly, almost inaudible above sound effects and voice, for the entire game, and sadly, the score may as well not be there at all.

Similarly, liberally applying music too late in the production process, towards the end, will result in this same kind of emotional wallpaper, or even worse as a Band-Aid solution, that is used in an attempt to fix what may be missing in the gameplay experience. Just because a combat sequence has high-tempo action music doesn't make the combat fun or exciting if the combat isn't fun or exciting. In this case, the music is telling the player something that isn't true, which is the antithesis of what music should be doing in a game – and we quickly lose trust in what the music is telling us.

The issue at play here is that if music is brought in too early and used for everything emotional at the expense of both sound and voice (where necessary) then music will quickly start, even in these earliest stages, to become relied upon to do this. This leads, inevitably, to music needing to be added to every piece of concept art that is produced, every video, every demo, every prototype, and once the game itself begins to take shape, as soon as production or feature development and benchmarking begins, music will be expected to be present in these same ways that it has been used in concept.

'We need music' is perhaps the first warning sign that originates in the design or cinematic departments very early on in their process. My counter to this is that we will wait, add sound, add voice, and then music will be last element that we add. The inclusion of music on prototypes is very often not even to give the player any real sense of feedback, but a 'mood wrapper', there to give the illusion that the feature is more finished and polished than it is. In this sense, it is always good to leave out music, so that it is clear to everyone playing a prototype that this is not intended to feel polished and finished. Music is often reached for as cake decoration, rather than as any kind of meaningful emotional or systemic feedback tool for the audience. Where emotion *is* needed to be prototyped and benchmarked, then music is entirely necessary to highlight emotion, but this very often occurs in the L2 or even L3 phases of a feature. When reached for directly and immediately in L1, the integration of music can come off as generic, mechanical and obvious, and it leaves little space at all for sound and voice development.

When original composed music is brought in too late in the process of development, and where temp music has been used as a crutch throughout concept and pre-production, the composer has very little to do. This becomes not so much of a composer's job, but the job of someone to come in and emulate already existing music. It is of course possible to create something new and original even against the backdrop of pre-existing temp score, however, because of the emotional *stickiness* of music when it is embedded for so long in cinematics, gameplay and trailers, it cannot easily be removed and replaced without the creative team feeling that any new music is changing the meaning and tone too drastically. Inevitably, the gravitational pull of the temp music, will continue to exert its power, long after being removed and replaced. The composer's job then becomes to simply replace the temp music with a legally acceptable simulacrum or soundalike. I always lament the creative opportunities that were lost on projects where this has been allowed to happen.

As a director, I would much rather work with a composer through the entire process, starting, very freely, with the overarching identity and emotional ideas behind the story and the gameplay. Then moving into specifics of feedback for mechanics and any other fundamental gameplay needs. All the time making the case for areas of the game where music will not play a role and will not be needed. After this, once a story is available and understandable, mapping out the musical themes and arcs that are necessary to develop and transition that musical identity from start to finish. Finally, towards the end of production, we would again work to *remove* as much of the music as possible – the cues that are not doing anything, or very little, or perhaps the cues that are diminishing the power of other sound moments, or other earlier or later music cues. Most composers would agree that if a music cue is not really doing anything other than getting in the way, then it should be removed. The final result, idealistically, though almost always never in practice, would be an experience in which the musical score represents about one third of the overall soundtrack of the game in terms of emotional, narrative and gameplay experience.

Instead of following the trends of spending less money and less time on more music, we should be doing precisely the opposite; more money and more time on less music.

18 Defining the sound

Towards an iconic music design

Identity is extremely important in video game creation. In a hugely competitive environment, every game has both the desire and the need to stand out and, ideally, have an instantly identifiable, and own-able, aesthetic. In this chapter we will explore some of the ways in which music, and in particular instrumentation and tone, as well as themes, can be used to create a unique identifiable and memorable element to any game, or franchise.

Main theme or main musical identity

Achieving an identity through music that becomes associated with a game, is extremely important and a strong element of the *overall identity* of a title.

Developing musical identity is an extremely fluid and creative process, one that rests entirely on the composer, the team and the game project. However, there are some basic approaches that seem to be fundamental when it comes to creating an identity that embeds music to a game's identity.

Usually, a main theme is valuable as a very quick way of conjuring the identity and feel of a game. A theme may be heard many times throughout the game, in association with perhaps a main character, or with the overall idea of world itself. When considering some of the ways that marketing and brand teams look at this kind of asset, a theme is used to identify and *differentiate* the game in the marketplace and ideally is easy to recognise and should differentiate from competitive titles. Given the amount of games released every year, this is not a simple ask.

Thinking less about marketing and more about the game, a theme would encompass *overall* what the game is about, and how the player feels when immersed in that world. Whether that takes in the main underlying elements of the story, or whether that conjures the feeling of exploring a vast world, it would ideally summarize what it means to be immersed in the world, and the kind of action and events that take place there.

Such a theme can also develop into a long-term element employed across multiple entries in a franchise and can be re-used or reimagined in various different musical arrangements or contexts to signify the shifting locale or emotional focus of the game.

By hooking this music directly into the differentiators within the game itself, the things that make the game unique, will supply inspiration and ideas for the kinds of musical short-cuts and information about the tone and mood and content of the world itself.

Recognisable and familiar, with a unique ingredient

One such common approach is that the musical theme material should be something that already feels comfortable and familiar to an audience, particularly if that audience is a *genre audience*, like Survival Horror or Action Adventure. Using a musical palette that is already established, familiar and successful is a good approach that allows a theme to welcome in a wide general audience for that particular genre, by echoing and signalling a lot of the tropes that they already expect. However, in order for *your* game to feel unique and for the music not to feel generic, there should always be a unique and *defining* ingredient, one that perhaps extends to the rest of the score in general. And again, that unique ingredient, whatever it is, should really resonate with the unique elements and approach or perspective, mood, or location, of the game itself. What is the twist? What is the most important defining feature? What is the X-Factor?

This could be an element of the setting or cultural inspiration in the game, like a specific iconic instrument found or used primarily in that locale. A great example of this is the choice of the Hardanger fiddle (*Hardingfele*) of Norway used in Austin Wintory's beautiful score for the game 'Pode'. The sound and the traditional performance of the main instrument create an identifiable sound that for a video game is unique, iconic and extremely beautiful, speaking to the emotional depth and meaning in the game first and foremost.

Additionally, the choice of sound could be a musical element that is present and important in the story itself, such as a glass harmonica used to attempt to cure the melancholy of a central character in a Victorian mystery exactly as can be found in one of the tracks in Carter Burwell's score for the motion picture, 'Mr. Holmes' (2015).

When we have an ingredient in the score that *resonates* in a powerful and evocative way with an element of the game world, or of the story, we have something that becomes much more of a shorthand for the game – a quick way to get across the feeling of the time and space where the game occurs, and also of some of the deeper sub textual themes within the game itself.

Whatever the choice, the *resonance* with the story and the world itself is critical. This might be something that on the surface is not obvious in the material but could bring a deeper meaning and overall perspective to the story arc. In this particular sense, I always think of the wonderful iconic juxtaposition of Gregorian chant in the Halo franchise, and the context of time and sacredness of the covenant that this brings to the sci-fi setting. It is almost like the score is there to provide the backstory to the entire universe of Halo. There is also a traditional, humanising element that this kind of unexpected music brings to the game's setting which is able to underscore (bring into the subconscious mind) the huge scope and scale of the game's subject matter, by conjuring authentic traditions and elements of the past.

Very often an iconic musical texture or simple melody becomes the core musical element that carries the identity in a main theme. However, because of the stickiness of simple, catchy melodies, it can be quite dangerous to use the melodic elements frequently, and especially dangerous to have them looping in a main menu, or over a long portion of game-play with no change. As always, with any sound element, but especially with melodic musical material, an acute awareness of when the player becomes annoyed or irritated by a repetitive musical motif, is essential. A main theme, particularly one with a simple melodic hook, rather than being *overused*, ideally would be used in synchronisation with an extremely iconic moment, like a title reveal or a main character reveal, and then quickly retired to resurface only in similarly iconic moments later in the story or gameplay. Even with areas with looping music, like a main menu, the main melodic hook of a theme should perhaps only be played in the beginning introductory section, and then the looping element to follow contains only harmony and variants of the theme – quite simply this is done in order to *protect the main theme* from over-exposure to the audience and *preserve* its power and effectiveness. A melodic and iconic main theme is indeed a sacred element of identity and 'spectacle' in a game's score and should be only used when the appropriate 'wow' moment is required. Music score in general is special, and should be reserved for important moments, but a main theme is a whole other level of 'special', that should be reserved and protected to amplify and resonate with absolutely critical iconic, memorable and spectacular moments in the game itself – *not looping every 30 seconds during a loading sequence or during mundane gameplay.*

19 The shape of emotion
We can't feel emotion all the time

As already alluded to, one of the weakest elements of video game music commissioning, direction and planning, is when music is designed or required to be played continually throughout the entire experience. This is fundamentally an approach where game music simply *follows requirements*, rather than leading and helping to *set* those requirements. Sometimes music is commissioned to be present even when the reason for it to be there is not clear, there should just be 'some music' here. This is often referred to as 'filler', just some musical texture that isn't really doing anything – just sitting there and soaking up bandwidth. This may be because the directors do not yet know what the important element is, the solution to which is to go and figure that out, before commissioning music to support or lead a scene that doesn't always require music. The music may be removed later, when all the other elements finally come together, at the end of production, and by 'removed' I mean either removed entirely, or, pushed to the back of the mix, so that it is at the bottom of the hierarchy of importance of audibility.

This continual approach is often one of the worst abuses of music, the effect being generally very negative, not only on the music itself, but also on the game and on the audience.

In a beautifully simple illustrative example, the composer Takeshi Furukawa related to me an incident where a friend of his used to highlight passages in a book as part of their study, but by the end, the amount of highlighted sections looked like the entire book was highlighted. The only thing standing out were the *unhighlighted* passages. Music, and the use of music to emphasize and *illuminate* emotion, is very similar to the use of that highlighter pen, and one can see that when it is overused, it starts to become a hindrance, and contradiction, to the very thing being highlighted.

That word, illumination, is extremely important in my approach to music, and I love thinking of music in this way. In 2019, I was fortunate enough to attend an exhibition of William Blake's illustration work at the Tate Britain gallery in London, and the extraordinary beauty, detail and emotion of the images was breath-taking. The thing that stood out to me was that Blake referred to the illustration work as *illuminated* texts, not as illustrated texts. And the word illumination, describing a light shining on, emphasising and exaggerating the meaning and beauty of the text, allowing us to not only *see* the texts, but to *feel* them and *experience* them. This is such an apt way of thinking about music, and what it really is bringing to a game – especially one that already has so much happening on screen and in the soundtrack. This illumination of emotion and feeling, making legible the heart of the game for the audience – through music, what we cannot see now made 'visible'.

As I understand it, there is also a similar trend in Hollywood cinema for more music with which to cover more of a film. With this too, even in a relatively short 90-minute experience, where the movie is giving us editorial emotional highlights of a particular story – music throughout, acting as anaesthetic – would almost certainly lead to a kind of *emotional paralysis and fatigue* in the audience – quite simply no longer being able to feel any significant emotional reaction, no matter what the score does to wake us up.

Granted, depending on the *type* of game experience being created, there may well be cases where music could be desirable to have play more continually (for example, in mobile or arcade game experiences where short jump-in jump-out gameplay is the designed method of play for an audience, rather than longer story arcs or chapters). However, even here, we may need to consider where it is better to coordinate elements of space and 'musical stillness' where music isn't continually present or required.

Emotional overwhelm

As an audience, we cannot feel intense emotions of the kind that are often shown onscreen, on such extreme scale of musical expression, continually and constantly. Spending what is probably a relatively small music budget on accompanying some of the more mundane aspects of the gameplay is probably going to result in a very thinly spread veneer of emotional accompaniment. In fact, if you are thinking about music budgets, you could consider your music budget as an 'emotion budget', and as such you might likely prioritize things in quite a different way.

Continual emotion, or the suggestion that a character and an audience can continually experience emotions is to ignore the quite natural fatigue, and the need to process emotional information, that comes with emotional experiences. This is another reason why I would argue there needs to be development and change in themes *over time* to depict the development of the characters in the game over the course of their journey. This means that the character at the beginning cannot have the same thematic material played in the *same way* with the same arrangements as they do at the very end. The musical themes need to go somewhere, if they are in any way to *represent* the development and growth of the character emotionally.

In 'Shadow of the Tomb Raider' (2018), the thematic material (written by Brian D'Oliveira) develops quite dramatically from the beginning ('Prologue & Overture'), starting with very dark and emotionally isolated, inward-facing strings and orchestral textures, signifying Lara's upbringing (a classical

European education and lineage). Her emotional issues with her family are at the centre of her obsessions as we begin the game. By the end of the game's story, we hear completely transformed arrangements of this same thematic musical material (entitled 'Goodbye Paititi'), now using instrumentation of Latin America (the location for the game), and now given vocal expression (emotion is now able to be *externalized* and expressed) by a young girl's voice (representing the re-birth of Lara's inner child) – showing that this character is now facing the world with an open heart – that the *young Lara* who we thought was gone, is healed. Musically and emotionally, we have gone from dark, internalised obsession, to openly expressed joy and celebration using the same musical motif. This thematic transition is used to articulate the narrative arc and development of the character on that journey through the musical devices chosen. It is a musical interpretation and expression of the story and its underlying themes.

By thinking of music as a skin, not as an *outer element* that we 'see', but as an *interface* between the outer world and the emotional world underneath which carries information between the two, we should be able to convey how the character reacts to and processes events in the world, but also how, through emotion, the character is able to express emotion and *cause* change in the outer world.

Musical stillness, not silence

In a similar sense to how sound and ambience takes a rest in stillness, rather than complete silence, music can also gear-down in quite similar ways. When the frequency and scale of musical events calms, and the score is able to die back to a more ambient state, we could say that the music becomes still. Given the emotional rollercoaster of continual emotional spikes in many games, musical stillness is something important to understand and make use of – the musical equivalent of resting or preparing to transition to a music-less state. All this can be achieved while maintaining the overall mood – giving the audience time to process those prior emotional and intensity spikes.

Ambient background music which relies on subtle tone and texture, rather than melodic, harmonic and dynamic movement, can be extremely effective at certain moments in video games because it allows the listener this respite from often complicated and stressfully complex thematic content.

The reduction of, or exclusion of percussive and higher tempo rhythmic elements, may be an initial way of offering respite for the player. This idea then of stillness in music, is a useful one when determining an area that is not entirely yet *devoid* of music, is less *gameplay* intensive, yet still requires emotional engagement for the player to focus on other things. It can act as a bridging device between action or engagement and no music, giving a more graceful method of transitioning down and back up, from no music to intense musical content.

Great examples of this kind of ambient music are within UI menus, where a player is expected to spend time managing resources and settings, often very strategically through pages of information. So a musical stillness here, perhaps conjuring a subtle 'mood' through an elongated series of sparse tonal chords, can help to continue the idea and presence of the emotional game world, but also to get out of the way of the players main strategic activities and focus. Subtle music movement can be built into these ambient pieces, in order to stretch them over the longer periods of time a player is likely to spend in these situations.

Similarly, in moments of exploration and contemplation *in-game*, offered by some of the opportunities in open world games, as the player explores vast open environments. The introduction of this kind of still ambient music, can entice the player into a meditative state of mind, in which the beauty and awe of the environment can be foregrounded and enjoyed, without being made to feel the need to engage in 'action' or activities where time is otherwise a factor in gameplay. This is a way of music getting out of the way and allowing other elements of the soundtrack to occupy the foreground. What I particularly love about this kind of musical treatment is that it doesn't *need* to engage all the melodic thematic elements that we may hear in more prominent music cues, but it can sit underneath sound, dialogue and general player activity in a way that is still supported by an emotional *perspective*. Not all musical cues and presence will be bombastic or attention grabbing, music can be present in extremely subtle, fragile and delicate ways, and still have a potent effect.

In the end, it comes down to how much *space* we are giving the player to both *think* and to explore their own feelings in relation to the content being depicted. Beautiful still moments, particularly in the aftermath of big, exciting, highly interactive set-pieces, allow this kind of contemplation, recovery and exploration of the player's own experiences and feelings. This is yet another wonderful opportunity of connection between player and the game itself, where a player can become deeply and emotionally invested in the world onscreen.

20 Diegetic, non-diegetic and trans-diegetic musical spaces

While in previous chapters in the sound section we explored the many layers of the diegetic space on to which clarity and ambiguity can be enacted, music similarly has these notions of the diegetic and non-diegetic, though weighted more towards the non-diegetic in terms of score. While certainly one of the most talked about elements, music in games certainly isn't just about non-diegetic 'score' – there are potentially many opportunities for different species of musical material in a game experience. We must consider then, the various diegetic categories of music that can exist in our titles.

A note on music supervision in games

Firstly, it is worth considering the environment in which music is being commissioned. On the audio team, a music director, or music supervisor is a reasonably recent and newly emerged role. The role encompasses the commissioning and coordination of *all* elements of the music in the game, not just score, but also of any licensed music and original or licensed *diegetic* musical elements in the game world (often referred to as 'source music'). All this music should ideally be considered *as a whole*, from an aesthetic, and also from a production and budgetary, standpoint.

In terms of licensed music that may appear in the game world, the aesthetics work in a similar way to which a music supervisor in film or television will find connection and resonance with the story and the world. As well as making sure those selections make sense in terms of the time period or the location represented in the game, the supervisor will ensure the psychological meaning placed on those pieces of music by the characters who are experiencing or controlling those diegetic musical moments supports the storytelling.

At the same time, some other practical areas that a music supervisor may be looking into are the musical selections for trailers and marketing campaigns, which can often be at odds with the musical direction adapted and decided for the game itself. Depending on the nature of the marketing campaign and the culture of the marketing team, or even the proximity of the marketing team to the game team, much discussion should be had on this topic to ensure selections are appropriate from both marketing and game aesthetic viewpoints.

Psychological meaning in the diegesis

Diegetic source music is quite commonly used in games and is an effective way to create *controlled musical spaces* inside a game world in which the characters themselves can hear, react and interact with the musical material. Music placed in the diegetic world itself can inform and tell us about the kinds of sonic environments that a character perhaps wishes to surround themselves with, so we are asked to read into that character's psychologically projected status. Music choices made by character's themselves can project a big outward part of their personality if music is used in an environmental and controlled setting, *by* that character. It can be used to give the impression of full control over one's environment, or perhaps also other emotional effects that this onscreen personality wishes to project. Similarly, characters who find themselves in environments where music is already played, could wish to hide certain elements of themselves, such as characters who wish to do clandestine business or deals, meeting in a private booth at a loud disco in Miami in the early 1980s. Diegetic music is a kind of environmental set dressing in its own right – and it telegraphs cultural meaning. Perhaps the music heard in the environment is part of a deep subcultural identity, this again speaks directly about the kind of people that this music attracts, and the kinds of people it repels, through its cultural sub messaging and engagement. Similarly, more villainous characters who are found in beautiful villas with classical piano or opera music playing, are very likely to be attempting to lend themselves a seriousness which they crave on a deep level within their psyche – also to put forward the idea that they are more educated and cultured, when quite often, the opposite is the case. So, we have choices of music to make that are story and character driven environmental set dressing, and it is the *character* who is speaking through the music that is positioned around them in the game world.

Of course, diegetic music can also be controlled by the player, even if it is all preselected by the 'character'. In a racing game example, one could choose to modify a playlist that is listened to in the car while driving. As the 'driver' of the vehicle, the players themselves are choosing the kind of psychological music that fits their approach to a high pressure, high performance race. But the selections that are *available* have all been pre-made to match the game's tone from the character standpoint. For some, calm, classical music or operatic music would be the perfect soundtrack to a high-octane car race or pursuit. For others it would be speed metal, and for others, 90s rave and so on. The music selection that is offered to the player, usually from a curated list provided by a music supervisor to fit in general aesthetic terms, the overall feeling and style of the title, can be further chosen as the emotional endpoint for the player.

Trans-diegetic music

Diegetic music can transition between being in the world, and audible to the characters, to a non-diegetic space, which becomes a kind of score to an action or emotional sequence. This is done most often in cinematic cutscenes or trailers, rather than in-game, whereby a character is seen to turn on a radio or play a record on a record player. We then hear the music played in the scene, with the reverb of the room, and then the music transitions to direct stereo, no longer in the 3D space with all its room reflection, but now occupying the inner non-diegetic space of the character's head. This presentation then serves to become the driving tempo and co-ordinating element of the ensuing action, including music-video style slow motion and hyper editorial moments. Time and space follow the logic of the music. Finally, perhaps at the end of the sequence, our musical perspective returns to the radio or record player in the room, as 3D source, before exiting the scene. This is certainly harder to do in the game engine with an interactive experience that cannot be orchestrated as easily as a cinematic can be, especially editorially, to the beats and crescendos of a piece of preselected, precomposed licensed music. However, it is not impossible to imagine a system that could approximate this kind of effect.

Inter-diegetic music

There is an additional category of diegesis for music, *inter-diegetic*, in which it is not explained whether the source of the music is in the diegetic environment, or whether it is a part of the score. One reference example I can give is from 'Shadow of the Tomb Raider', where in some of the Tomb and jungle environments, certain stems and elements of the score were removed from the stereo music cues, and placed in 3D into the game environments, so that they would pan around as the player moved through those spaces. These elements, often more musical 'effect' stems of the score, were things that *could* almost be considered sound effects, unfamiliar elements like breaths, or death whistle sounds, or low clay instrument drones, and they were not synced up with the score's tempo in any meaningful way. The effect however introduced a deliberate feeling of uneasiness and self-questioning on the part of the player. This turned out to be one of the key effects of our definition of 'fear' in the game – to introduce this kind of ambiguity and uncertainty about the reality of what was audible in the environments, and represented a real physical warning or threat, or whether they were sounds psychologically produced in Lara's imagination, and by extension the imagination of the player. Once implemented, this effect created a great sense of uneasiness and cautiousness in some of these dark, terrifying and deadly environments. We also had very dense Amazonian jungle environments in the game, which similarly enabled us to play with the idea of not quite being sure what it was you were *hearing* or were *imagining,* In a sense this was a way of us confronting directly the notions of a score that was not audible to the characters in the world but one that then gradually became semi-materialized in the 3D environment – particularly an environment shaped by a Maya and Aztec culture whose ghostly presence demanded that the score shifted continually from the imagination into reality.

What we describe here is a way of deliberately turning some of the conventions of diegetic and non-diegetic music against one another in order to create a tension about how to feel about what is onscreen in the game. By moving 'music' score elements around in the 3D space, we are suggesting that the music has somehow ruptured through the diegetic membrane and is now bleeding into that real physical location, and whatever is causing that music, is somehow present, and layered onto that location. I really love that we were able to explore this aspect of an incredible ancient culture that had all but disappeared, but that could be imagined to be still there, still present. This puncturing of the diegetic and non-diegetic space, creating a new inter-diegetic space was a perfect way to explore that feeling and that idea. When an audience enters this suspended 3D sound world, the psychology of a scene and the questioning of objective and subjective realities is one that proposed itself. It allows an audience to explore not only the physical space seen (and imagined in the dark shadows) onscreen as a representation of the game's reality, but now the game onscreen and the physical 3D space represented by that game onscreen can also be freely interpreted as a *3D exploration of a psychological or supernatural space*. Reality can be both suspended and still present here. If we think of the potential for this idea in other games, or in other similar worlds – for example, a character may see a ledge in the game, but the ledge may suddenly stretch to feel far away, and burst into flames as they approach it – the walls themselves may move, the physical space itself may reassemble and tell the player that they cannot fully trust what they see as a believable objective reality, but rather a psychological reality established and partly conjured through the imaginings of the character on screen. Any playable nightmare or dream sequence that is depicted onscreen could also play with more extreme elements of this concept, but we can also push the psychological states of the characters themselves by applying these states of mind when the character is wide awake – particularly if the character is in a heightened or vulnerable mental state.

Inter-diegetic music can be used to convey this rupture of the traditionally accepted boundaries of score and music in the diegesis, and of the traditionally accepted *sources* of musical score. I have noticed an increase in the use of this kind of music and sound interchange over the last ten or so years in video games. The themes of games where psychological states or ambiguity and mystery are primary creative concerns. Some fine examples are Playdead's 'Limbo', and perhaps more recently and on the more extreme end of the practice, Remedy Entertainment's 'Control'. Both play with these ideas of reality and imagined reality layered over each other, as well as memory, confusion and mystery. All this, while always exposing the player to a world in which almost nothing is explained up front to the player. Clarity is not a priority in these game worlds, ambiguity is a central device. It is critical to the effect, that the player joins in and enters into the investigative process about the reality of the world itself along with the character. In Limbo's case, the character is a boy with no words, and the acoustic world is expressed through sound as though through some special contact-apparatus that enables us to hear something occurring elsewhere – eventually, we hear a sonic *emotional presence*, which we could describe as 'music' but which doesn't really fit any traditional musical sound or role – all of this makes for a very natural feeling inter-diegetic experience. It is one that is not awkward or forced, it simply presents itself onscreen for the player to experience. In Remedy's 'Control', the character is very vocally articulate and talkative throughout the game, and the interchange and continual switching between inner non-diegetic voices inside the character's head and spoken diegetic dialogue that other characters in the world can hear, is very free and fluid. Self-doubt and questioning are continual, and from the beginning moments of the game, we trust almost nothing we see or hear. The music and sound similarly participate in this free-flowing inter-diegetic exchange. The physical space of the game participates too, as we see the physical space shift and morph in front of our eyes, conveying this idea that there is perhaps no difference between a real or imagined experience in the Bureau, the game's central location.

One potential origin of these kinds of ideas is the horror genre of both cinema and games, and many techniques that have been used to terrify audiences have since become more commonly used with much fewer disturbing concepts in games that promote more of a mystery and adventure element. I think this movement denotes a significant shift in the opening up of these kinds of new realities, that simultaneously represent what is happening in the character's head as much as what is happening in the world itself.

Here, in the real world, with our own increasing ability to wield control over our sonic environments through technology and gadgets, as we curate and navigate music playlists that we hear on smaller and smaller in-ear headphones as we move around our world – similarly the increasing technological reach and power available to us to stream music into every room in our homes, whether indoor or outdoor spaces, our sense of musical control over our environments is increasing all the time. We are perhaps already using too much music in our daily lives to attempt to modify, or regulate our emotions and moods, perhaps we are using it as a way of masking emotions or underscoring our social environments, perhaps we are using music as a way to try to assume some control over our inner emotional worlds.

21 Non-diegetic space in recorded music

Another fascinating area of sonic space to consider is the space inherent in the recorded score itself, and how that translates to, and interplays with, the diegetic 3D game-world spaces we see on screen.

It could be argued that by having music recorded in a recognisably reverberant live space, perhaps an interesting cathedral or cave, one which imprints the space into the recording of the music in an interesting and characterful way, there could be a dissonance with the 3D reverberated spaces that are presented in the diegesis of the game, for example a cave or tomb. Perhaps the spaces match and they become too resonant giving the impression the musical score is originating from the onscreen space itself, or conversely, perhaps they do not align and become too dissonant, though it rarely seems to cause a problem.

There are a few reasons why the ear is perhaps not particularly too bothered by non-diegetic space embedded in music. I believe first and foremost it is that we have become accustomed to non-diegetic space being present in musical scores, and almost all kinds of music in general, especially genres of popular music, over the entire history of recorded music. Certain genres of music even carry with them an expectation for the presence of some kind of musical performance space or production-added space. Cuban music very often only feels authentic when the presence of a mid-sized hall or room is audible in those recordings. Similarly, choral and classical music will almost always be recorded in large live-sounding spaces. One could argue that the most *unnatural* setting for music is within a studio where all the reflections and performance space is removed, and the sound is 'dead' without the imprint of a live space. This is also perhaps the reason why, almost immediately, during the production of most kinds of music, artificial reverb is added back to isolated vocals, drums and other instruments, in order to get back some kind of feeling of air moving in an *actual space*.

Exaggerated space

In such recordings, the reverberation that is added is very often exaggerated and does not necessarily match anything we would be used to hearing in terms of a live performance. Giant reverbs on vocals, or echo delay effects take our ears and imaginations into performance spaces that are fantastical and spectacular – used more perhaps as sweeteners and unique signatures of the music or performance, rather than the authentic fingerprint of any real-world performance space.

Combined spaces

In this same sense of artificially constructing performance spaces around recordings that have been made in isolation, in which more mix and creative control can be gained over each individual element – when the reverb and space effects are added back into the music – they can be applied either to the entire 'band', or to only specific elements of that band. This is why we get vocal reverbs the are completely different from drum reverbs and again, completely different from the bass (most often dryer) and guitar reverb spaces and effects. This mélange of different effects could be mainly to do with production techniques in which all the elements of a band are 'produced' in such a way as to create the idea a much larger sound stage (meaning that each element occupies not only the frequency and timbral domain of the spectrum, but is extended and magnified into ranges that they wouldn't normally occupy). Vocals for example only occupy a small, but critically important frequency range around 1000 KHz, yet, through reverb and vocal effects, the space which they occupy, and the implied projection and reach of those vocals, can be fully controlled and changed as the song progresses.

By producing each element with its own reverb and spatial identity, we also separate each element and give them their own unique 'location' in the sound stage. So, this spatial construct then, in music and performance, can be about defining individuals with very different identities in the same band, coming together in performance. Different genres certainly have very different approaches to this kind of constructed space – again, coming back to Cuban music, in which an actual authentic performance space is used to cement all those performers together in the same place, we hear them as part of the same community, in that same space, together, with a solidarity and equality to the sound. Similarly, other genres may eschew the notion of artificial reverb or what can sometimes be referred to as 'over production' such as the many sub-genres of metal – in which a single live performance is simply recorded in as raw a way as possible, and is far more important to both the artist and their audiences, than any production manipulation. It is certainly not a big deal to an audience that the vocal and the drums in a piece of music occupy different 'spaces', it does not cause the audience to become confused about this space in which they may or may not be.

Dynamic artificial space

Not only are these manufactured spaces capable of being artificially constructed *per instrument*, they are also able to be changed dynamically to match different sections of a song – for example an intimate vocal style verse, very close to the microphone, not projected very loudly, can be made to sound the same level as a chorus that is now sung and projected extremely loudly from a more distant mic position that takes in a lot more of the room and the increased reflections, whether real or artificially added. We may have then, a dynamic interplay of intimate, personal, and privately expressed vocal elements, followed by loud, projected proclamations, shouted on high, exaggerated through *dynamic* application of space. These dynamics of space give the performance somewhere to go and somewhere to return to and begin to take on some elements of spatial storytelling. And so, we can start to unfurl how space, both authentic and implied, in recorded music is used, and expected, to communicate certain psychological elements and pronouncements about a song, and a performance.

Certainly, some of these same cultural learnings and expectations apply to how we listen and understand the spatial storytelling that is happening in video game scores, though perhaps less consciously than if we listen to the OST (Original Sound Track) only. Artificial orchestral samples with the addition of cathedral like reverb space can trick the ear into thinking that the 'orchestra' is really there and is performing in an authentic cathedral space. This feeling of spatial consistency is where the reverb is being used to democratise everything that we hear, all the individual instruments are treated as a single entity 'the orchestra' in a single space, and not as individual elements that are identifiable and recognisable through their own reverbs like we referred to in the genre music examples.

To this end, musical scores which incorporate non-diegetic space into their 'sound' have never to my knowledge, proven to have any adverse effects on the audiences *misreading this as diegetic space* in the game world – providing that the space in the music is clear that it belongs to the musical recording. The coexistence of multiple 'spaces' across the diegetic and non-diegetic spectrum, emphasises this dichotomy of a real-world space which is represented through the proposed diegesis onscreen, *and* an imagined space inside the character's or player's head, in which the music, or emotion is present. The exception to this might be if elements within the score are excessively panned around in 3D – thus placing the instruments into the inter-diegetic space discussed earlier. Though the panning in musical scores is likely not controlled by the player, doing so could become confusing as to what the cause of the panned sound is.

While not music, we also hear this same non-diegetic space explored in terms of its reflective properties in representations of the presence of an 'inner voice' or a 'voice remembered from memory' through the addition of long reverb effects to that voice. This realm of the inner imaginary seems to line up well with the idea of a space that is equivalent to acoustic spaces that represent the sacred – churches, large caves, and echoic valleys which are revered for their spiritual connectedness. Perhaps the voice, this inner voice of memory, simply needs some way of making sure that the audience doesn't confuse the voice with an actual voice occurring in the real space of the world onscreen – thus the reverbs are exaggerated greatly to place its cause *beyond* the screen. It is also interesting to note that reverb applied to intimate, close voices, has an unnatural otherworldly effect, as we are used to only hearing such reverbs excited by louder more projected vocal performances. Therefore, intimate and quiet voices, close to the microphone, with reverb added, will often sound and feel otherworldly or unnatural. So, it follows to some extent with music, this idea of a sacred space is where much classical orchestral music tends to occur in our experience of concert repertoire and recorded concert repertoire. Indeed, the history of western music is built on the notion of music as divine and sacred. The non-diegetic space of the recording plays its role in adding a consistency to the overall sound of the score, which allows the player, once they acclimatise themselves to the 'sound world' of the score, to quite easily ascribe that space to the music, and not to the 3D diegetic space represented on screen. But also, one of maintaining that historical connection and feeling of the sacred and the divine to this *otherworldly* music, which has no apparent cause in the worlds we perceive onscreen.

One interesting area certainly worth mentioning, where non-diegetic space in music seems to not work as successfully, is in sections of gameplay where the player and camera are underwater. When all the sound of the diegesis changes to the underwater sound perspective, the presence of musical score, which has 'air' in it, does feel dissonant in the experience. In 'Shadow of the Tomb Raider', during the final mix, we decided to low-pass filter slightly the musical score during any extended underwater sequences, in order to match better the *overall* feeling of submersion and claustrophobia required onscreen. Again, this matched our vision of having the player uncertain whether what they were hearing was indeed a score or was a apart of the world itself – so by processing the score a little to carry the influence of being 'underwater' through pressure or presence, we were able to similarly imply that the score (inside Lara's head) was also in some way being pressured by the water itself.

There is certainly much creative scope to further explore these areas of non-diegetic space being affected by what is happening onscreen in this same manner as the underwater example. Widening or exaggerating reverbs on the music dynamically so that it connects with what is happening on screen in terms of emotional changes or shifts in the character's feelings or perceptions. For example, we may hear a distant reverberant song or mysterious solo voice, bathed in reverb and echo as though it is very far away at the beginning of a game – denoting some mystery. And by the end of the game, the voice is now clearer, more intimately recorded, and even has words that we can now discern giving a poetic meaning of the character or story of the game. This kind of dynamic use of *spaces* in a score to deliver meaning and the development of thematic material – especially as it relates to the transitioning of concepts present in the game's story – opens up powerful avenues for spatial storytelling in the non-diegetic realm of the score.

The diegetic space in music is wide open, and we can use it as another creative avenue for storytelling. It is a vastly under-explored realm that can be defined and investigated to the extent that we want it to be. Because it represents the emotional world of our characters, and by extension, of our players, it remains capable of both clarity and ambiguity as much as we need it to be.

Spatial non-diegetic music

As mentioned in the previous chapter, spatial elements in the musical score can sometimes potentially offer up certain challenges when layered onto an already existent 3D diegetic world, such as panning instruments around in the score when the music is used in the context of a 3D game space.

One area in particular that presents a problem in that regard is the spatialisation, or precise localisation, of musical sources into 3D. Particularly problematic is where music is anchored to the 3D space, so that as the player moves the camera around and while exploring the diegetic space, the musical space also rotates and locks to the diegetic compass points of the game world.

Where this kind of spatialised music is more successful, or stands less chance of confusing an audience, is if the musical sources are 'spread' into more diffuse areas of sound, ones that cannot be as precisely located in the actual diegetic 3D space. For example, if we are able to precisely locate where a violinist in the score is located in the 3D score space, and we approach that place, we would expect to find something emitting that music in the diegetic space, actually we would expect to find a violinist. At this point, we start to believe in and experience the music as a part of the diegesis presented onscreen, rather than a non-representational non-diegetic space that is implied and baked into the score. The more abstract the position of musical performers becomes, the more acceptable it is as a *3D spatialised score* that doesn't correspond to the diegetic space. Again, it is perfectly possible to imagine gameplay that is designed around rendering 3D music score as some kind of element with which players can use to navigate or locate something in the space. Ideally, the musical score shouldn't interfere with the primary objective of the 'player' audience, which is to have useful information from the diegetic world rendered and locatable in 3D – for example, telling the player that a threat is located in 3D space is far more important to the player's survival instincts, than it is to hear a piece of abstract non-gameplay relevant information represented in 3D space.

Like any effect, it is perhaps most successful to break these established rules of diegetic and non-diegetic music in very special and exceptional circumstances, only where perhaps a 'wow factor' is required. A moment in gameplay where the player enters a particular 'mode' of perception, for example, could be one area where the musical score 'becomes' more spatialised. In this 'mode' the player could then use these elements to navigate, or they could offer extra information about the space in this mode – or perhaps used simply to express the idea that the player's state of perception is changed, and that they are now able to navigate inside this 'emotional realm' of music.

Developing new layouts and spaces for 3D elements of the musical score is a wonderful opportunity to build a rapport with some of the ideas that may be inherent in the game's experiential or story dynamics, or indeed further representing ideas of the inner world of the characters. By elevating in height certain elements of the score, we may imply that the voices in a choir, for example, are coming from above us, and without *seeing* the choir perform and being able to locate them in this non-diegetic 3D space, we may infer that the voices and their reverberant sound is swirling above us from some divine location in the skies above us. Human hearing is especially tuned to pay attention to sounds above and behind, presumably as a way of threat detection. So, any music that emanates from these locations is sure to gain our attention, though ideally only on a subconscious level. Transient sounds, particularly sudden sounds in those elevations or surrounds, will cause a player to move the camera and try to investigate the cause of those sounds, so ambient musical sounds such as choirs with softer, less transient textures, could safely be placed in the overhead and surround positions without triggering the threat response.

So then, we might expand this field of spatial music, and challenge the traditional notion of a fixed listener, and a fixed position for the musical elements in the spatial field, to embrace perhaps height and surround channels, in a way that establishes the internal logic of the space of the score, without triggering unwanted threat responses in the player. Some areas to be cautious of are where identifiable musical sound sources can be accurately located in 3D space, as well as locking the rotation of non-diegetic musical 3D space to that of *diegetic* space, as this could also lead to confusion and *unintentional ambiguity* when it comes to giving the players clear spatial cues about threats or exploration opportunities in the diegetic 3D world. The degree to which the experience on screen is *abstracted* vs the degree to which it is a simulation of a 3D *reality* is always going to come heavily into play when it comes to a 3D score.

22 Leading with music

Music as spectacle throughout production and post-release

Finally, we will consider some ways of leading the production by taking advantage of some of the natural spectacles of music production that occur throughout the process of creating a score for a game.

Throughout production, as the musical score starts to come to life when working with a composer, there are a great many opportunities with which to engage and excite the rest of the team, as well any other interested internal parties about the content and production of the music.

This spectacle can range from highlight videos or play-throughs where just the music is soloed and foregrounded – so that the development team gets to hear just the music, rather than the music mixed in with all the other elements they would normally hear. Whenever I have done this, though it can mean some long stretches of silence, when the music comes in, it feels strangely like showing *just* the emotions in the game, almost like seeing things differently under a UV light, showing an abstracted and alternate version of the game with which most of the team will already be familiar, so it usually grabs attention.

If your score uses live musicians, once you get closer to recording those musicians it is always useful to continually gather and document the process with video footage if at all possible. Again, these are great elements that can be shown to the rest of the team in order to not only generate excitement but to reveal some of the secrets of how the musical sounds were created. This is also good for amassing a wealth of material that can also be used when the time comes to go public with some of these assets, and similarly excite and engage the game's fans about the craft behind the score that has been created. Getting the chance to see things like virtuoso musicians performing on either a familiar or unusual instrument, generates a lot of excitement about the game and through highlighting the craft and skill that is going into it, exposing the process, you offer a chance to see elements of authenticity and passion in the production. It is easy to forget this, especially if you are involved on a daily basis in that world of music and the creation and implementation of those assets, but for someone outside of that world, it is extremely exciting and inspiring to see and hear these elements of creation and production. Very often this will inspire the other departments to create similar 'craft' focussed videos and presentations for the team, in order to similarly unveil and showcase the work and the research that is going on *behind the scenes*. It is becoming more valuable to record, document and maintain this kind of footage and knowledge about the craft approaches of how games are made. This kind of development footage seems to focus on areas of emotional production such as music performance, actor performance, Foley performance and sound effect creation, usually either in field locations or a spectacular studio – but there is also a lot of scope for pushing these kinds of craft focussed showcases for areas that are not so usually spotlighted. For example, collaborative work, discussions and the journey that a lot of these elements go on from start to finish. This under-documented aspect can offer a glimpse into the more realistic essence of how games are created and being able to document and show this kind of shaping and interaction, as the maps and features change, the characters evolve is not so commonly seen. This can be achieved for music by playing early sketches and comparing them with more advanced, finished orchestrated pieces of music. This celebration of the idea that the craft of game development is at its core collaborative and iterative, and that the music isn't something which is just successful first time and recorded. Beautifully filmed footage and interviews of full orchestral recordings in appealing surroundings is one thing, but it can give the somewhat false impression that the process is entirely like that, other than just a thin sliver of execution at the end. By showing and including references to the full process by which this moment was achieved, the overall impression could be even more spectacular.

By showcasing and sharing these early production, collaborative and writing elements of the music creation, ideation and recording process, there are great opportunities to excite and generate interest from the team. This can open up doors to collaboration opportunities that may otherwise have always remained closed. It is also a way of gearing up and rehearsing for the act of shining a spotlight on elements of the music production process once the game is released into the wild. I believe that having rehearsed these kinds of presentational opportunities all throughout production, and becoming more confident on camera and honing interview skills, also gaining familiarity with discussing the underlying *concepts* of the game's music – the team will itself become used to thinking about showcasing spectacle, and being able to frame their work in such a way that other team members are included and feel involved in this process of creating the music for the game. Other developers, unfortunately, can feel excluded and shut out from what is sadly, often a very closely guarded, secretive and personalised process between just a few members of the sound and creative team. By demystifying and opening up this process, the ideas influences and inspirations can flow, and you will certainly assemble more allies and interest from both within and outside the team, not to mention all the positive feedback that you can pass back to the composer, and music team.

There is tangibly a much higher level of excitement and interest among the audience for games about music than there is in for example, cinema audiences about the music for movies. This engagement is something that can absolutely be leveraged to huge advantage by the audio team in driving focus on the emotional elements of the game. This can open up areas of discussion about the game that are more centred on overarching themes being conveyed by the music - discussion of themes, and their meaning, can also open up ideas about how the developer would like the player to feel in the world, which is extremely valuable in any communication with the audience. There is a wider conversation about game music and emotion here that it is important and exciting to be a part of, where the audience for the game gets to give you *their* takeaways and impressions of the work. There are some avenues for this kind of feedback that are best avoided, such as comments sections on public videos, just to be aware that these encourage as much negativity as they do positivity. However, live panels and discussions can certainly take the place of these comments or message-board feedback situations for a more articulate interchange of ideas.

Part IV

Voice

Why do we need voice?

When we consider voice, perhaps more so than in sound and music, there is a strong line of inheritance in video game entertainment coming from cinema, all the way back through to theatre, opera and even further back into the pre-histories of storytellers around the campfire. Verbal storytelling is certainly an integral part of who we are and a defining part of the human experience itself. The *human voice* in which these stories are told occupies a podium position in the way our brains have evolved to prioritise sound – focussed to hear and foreground the audible frequencies, patterns and nuances of the human voice; we pay more attention and dedicate more brain resources to this sound than any other. We rely on the human voice for survival, for information, for psychological wellbeing, and can interpret minute sub-emotional subtleties, especially when face-to-face with another person, in a situation where this audible information can be put together with facial expressions, scents and body language. As a species, our ears and eyes are attuned so much to the voice, that we are able to notice even a few milliseconds of bad lip-sync, as well as instantly trusting or distrusting a speaker and the veracity of their words through the way they are spoken. Deeply embedded cultural markers are evident in the way we use words and compose sentences, in the dialects that are used, as well as the patterns, rhythms and choice of words – all these elements also serve to include or exclude listeners. We can speak *broadly* to all or narrow our speech and tone to very specific audiences through these choices. Spoken words are extremely powerful, they convey our intellectual and emotional inner worlds and intentions to the outer world – and they do this through sound. Words are a form of magic in the sense that we are able to shape reality through the conjuring of words and the importance we place on them. Words are formed inside us, and are projected out into the world, they are one of the strongest forms of self-actualisation – telling the listener who we are, through personality, emotion and intellect. People continually judge other people based on what they look like, and almost always get it wrong, however, when someone speaks *from the heart*, you get who they really are.

Interestingly, if we consider one of the most fertile periods of cinema history we can, with genuine validity, also ask the question 'do we need voice in this game?' There are many more examples of video games with no dialogue than there are with no music, or no sound effects. Some of the most popular and critically acclaimed games of *all time* feature no voice, from Fortnite's 'Battle Royal' – to 'Journey' – to 'Limbo' – to 'Inside' – to 'Tetris' – we can fill many pages with the names of these games. In this sense then, it seems that *excluding* voice brings something significant to the experience or, put another way, through the absence of speech, we allow space for something to happen in a game that isn't possible when a game includes spoken dialogue.

In the period between 1926 and 1932, just before and after the coming of commercially viable sync sound in cinema (in 1927), came the end of a period in which cinema had been evolving a visual storytelling language without synchronised voice. Many directors, including Fritz Lang, initially denounced the coming of sync sound as a death knell for the *art of cinema*, and indeed many actors and stars of the silent screen dreaded the coming of the 'talkies' as it surely meant that their cinematic art form, of *acting without voice*, would be destroyed.

All around the world, in the period prior to sync sound, there was an extremely broad and fertile period of visual storytelling in cinema, which ranged from the experimental films of Georges Meillies, to the visually opulent pre-revolutionary Russian cinema of Yvgenni Bauer. It is exceedingly difficult for us now, from our relatively noisy vantage point of the early 21st century, to imagine – in those few silent film reels that remain for us to view today – this art form from being anything more than an odd novelty, but these early films were the sensuous, experiential, entertainment blockbusters of their day.

Games, particularly indie games, but increasingly larger scale triple-A titles, continue to eschew spoken dialogue in favour of foregrounding a different form of voiceless, or at least wordless, narrative experience via *onscreen text*. These onscreen texts are sometimes, though not always, accompanied by a general, sometimes cartoony, approximation of speech in the form of wordless vocal sounds from the character speaking. In a similar way to onscreen text, most silent films used *inter-titles* which displayed both descriptions of the scenario and also any sparse dialogue that was to be emanating from the characters. It is worth considering also that voice, and dialogue do not *equate* to narrative. In 2017, the best Narrative category at the BAFTAs was won by the game 'INSIDE', which contained zero lines of spoken dialogue and no onscreen text aside from the main menu with which you initiated the game.

So while not essential to games, the use of dialogue presents a great many opportunities and challenges, not least of which is the pipeline through which the writing of lines of spoken dialogue, to the *hearing* and reviewing of that dialogue onscreen in the game, needs to be fully understood and made as frictionless as possible.

23 Early dialogue development

Establishing the plan

If you should find yourself working on a game that requires spoken dialogue, you are going to need a thorough understanding of the creative and technical workflow, as well as a serious plan in place, to produce and realise that dialogue. Dialogue can be at the centre of almost all elements of the game from budgetary, to creative, to design, to technical. It is almost always at the centre of the entire collaborative vortex of game development and can be pushed and pulled in many different directions by different disciplines, and by different personalities with very strong opinions on projects. Dialogue is often necessary to provide the player with the correct information and feedback. It can also be necessary to communicate the emotional aspects of the story, as well as the evolving personalities of the characters, in order to deepen the connection that the player feels with those characters. It is also extremely important from an implementation, mix and priority perspective in terms of audibility of the right types of dialogue at the right time – as part of an ever-changing dynamic context.

Establishing design and aesthetics

Many different aspects will be captured by dialogue; before thinking about casting and recording, we really need to figure out how dialogue is required to function in the game and what role it will play – what is the design and what are the storytelling aesthetics that are needed. These two areas, the design and the aesthetics, the *information* and the *emotion*, are essential in setting up the rest of the production. The answer to these questions is often to be found in *prototypes* that demonstrate functionality, and *benchmarks* that demonstrate emotion and aesthetics. For each of the dialogue features in the game it is absolutely essential to go through this process – learning the structure of dialogue systems, and also how many lines, and variations of those lines, are needed. These prototypes and benchmarks will also help to determine what exposition is too long for the player to follow in certain situations, if paired with action gameplay for example, as well as what kinds of performance are required so that the player feels like they are part of the story unfolding onscreen.

The design department will usually drive the systemic aspect of the dialogue features as well as the prototyping done in that regard, as it will be almost entirely functionality focussed. The aesthetics will be more determined by the benchmarking, built after the functional prototype is satisfactorily achieved, and on top of that system, by exploring actual performance with actors, built on top of the functional prototype – together these two ideas focus on the way in which the writers and actors and characters onscreen deliver that *emotive information* to the player through performance.

As with sound and music, there are many different forms that dialogue may take: is it onscreen character dialogue? What are the characters saying and why? Is it *information* driven dialogue, or situational and emotion-driven performances? Is it systemic barks, and are there additional contextual barks? Or perhaps non-interactive linear cinematics, is it interactive conversation in the style of choice-driven cinematic sequences? Each one of these types of dialogue, and perhaps many more besides, will require different approaches to writing, performing and triggering the content.

As mentioned, many of these different approaches can be figured out primarily through a rapid iterative prototyping phase, in which temporary dialogue is written and tested inside a quick mock-up of the intended feature. This way your team can relatively easily figure out what works and what doesn't work from an audio playback point of view (it is impossible to critique and properly iterate on paper-only designs of this nature, only when a feature is playable, in rough form, onscreen can you begin to pull apart what works and what doesn't and why). The team is able to judge and make note of whether certain lines are too long, or too short, or the cadence and intensity of dialogue structure feels right or wrong. It is also at this point that you can already determine if the dialogue triggers start to feel repetitive (when the same event, and line, may be triggered on multiple occasions) and you can develop an understanding of how deep the *variations* for particular kinds of dialogue events will need to be.

This kind of early prototyping may possibly be an area where synthesised machine-learning generated voices can play even more of a role in the iterative development of a script, *prior* to getting it in front of real actors. The more a script can be worked, re-worked and finessed at the writing stage, to get to the core of what needs to be said informationally, the better, and ideally, these enriched scripts can *then* be placed into the actor's hands in order to more fully realize the performance and characterisation elements of the lines.

24 The sound of voice

Dialects, culture and meaning

Accents and dialects carry a great deal of meaning and narrative information about a character, or even about a product, through narration to convey the *tone* of your title. Diverse dialects in class-driven societies such as the United Kingdom also bring with them the inherent cultural implications and stereotypes of wealth, education as well as societal and political stratification, even if that is not inherently understood fully in the target audience (e.g. North America) – there can still be broad differentiation by association (a well-spoken Received Pronunciation dialect used on a ruling character in a fantasy game, compared with a northern accent used for the heroic under-dog who rises to challenge them, will reinforce these meta narratives of class and political division in fictional worlds too). This stereotyping, typecasting and re-enforcement of class roles has been going on for so long now that anything that goes against the grain can either feel poorly cast, or if done deliberately in co-ordination with many other factors of the narrative or character arc, innovative. As an example, any audience familiar with Fantasy cinema from the 1970s onwards will also have inherited a expectation of this model of class-driven casting and stereotyping, and indeed will most likely expect it to be replicated to some extent in video games – as a continuation of popular culture from cinema. This is certainly because games function in the continuum of general popular culture and conventional shorthand, that can be quickly understood by audiences, and this continues today in not just games, but across most newly commissioned TV content.

Rather than focus too much on dialects and stereotypes, there are instead two broad modes of speech performance that underpin most approaches to video game performance, regardless of dialect and content – those of naturalism and informational clarity.

Perfect speech: informational clarity

When we hear speech that is perfectly articulated and fully formed, not just in sentences, but in complete paragraphs, it is an indicator of either someone who is saying something that has been prepared and rehearsed, delivering a message that has long been formulated and composed, *or* from someone who is reading the words out from an auto-cue or prepared script. This mode of speech can have very few elements of spontaneity or improvisation, and is free of repeating elements, rephrasing, corrections, digressions, non-sequiturs or false starts. When heard, it allows us to listen and receive the information *clearly* as intended and comprehend it more precisely. However, we tend to understand that we are receiving something that is not necessarily delivered from or representing the *heart and emotion* of the person delivering it in that moment. So while this mode of speaking is better for delivering information (we may hear police dispatchers speaking in this very clear, calm, information-first way also, even in extreme conditions) it often lacks elements of character, personality, emotional trust and sincerity.

Vernacular, or emotional speech

When an idea is being formed and articulated *in the moment*, or as an emotional *reaction* to something that is happening in that moment, perhaps as part of an emergent conversation or exchange of ideas, we tend to hear a very different pattern of speaking. The words are often repeated, paraphrased and rephrased, sometimes with many repeated words or concepts, and perhaps after quite some time, ending with a kind of summary of what has been said such as '...so what I'm really trying to say is...'. This kind of speech also represents that a thought is in motion and is being formed and produced in the moment that we are hearing it. False starts, stammering, drifting off topic, interruptions from another person who is in the conversation, result in a much more fractured 'text' if we were to write it down verbatim, that is often unclear and unrefined. However, this mode of speaking more often conveys a message that is delivered with emotion and authenticity of the person speaking in terms of how they *really feel* in that moment. In this mode, we can hear someone thinking and their thought process. So, the listener will get the sense that the words are a more true and honest representation of the feelings and emotions of the person speaking.[1] There are also cultural elements of vernacular speech that can be integrated into the way a character speaks, common phrases or sounds that are attached to the ends of sentences like '...*you know what I mean?*' which when combined with a dialect, can denote quite specific urban or rural sources for the voice we are hearing – imparting that they are an authentic part of a culture.

Our brains are easily able to detect and pick up these cues and meanings from both methods of speaking – in combination with some visual cues, it is one of the reasons we trust certain people and distrust others – but it is also one of the reasons that character actors are able to fool the listener into *believing* that the lines that they are saying are not pre-written and pre-determined, but that they are genuine reactions that are being produced spontaneously in the moment.

Much of video game performance and writing is still firmly rooted on the side of prioritising and delivering clear information to the player. As long as this remains a priority, there can be very little room for improvisation or for vernacular speech that allow lines to feel more hesitant and improvisational, though that is certainly changing. This perhaps also has a lot to do with why, in popular culture, many video game characters and performances have a very stiff and formal animatronic feel to them, as recently parodied in the reboot 'Jumanji' movies ('Welcome to the Jungle' (2017) and 'The Next Level' (2019) with Rhys Darby's *Nigel* character).

This animatronic feel also has a lot to do with line repetition. The amount of line variations that are necessary for dialogue to appear more convincing and natural is also a lot more than most video game writers and creators are committed to producing. Repetition can be especially problematic in systemic events that occur constantly throughout the game, for example a combat category of dialogue in which a character taunts their enemies – the player will spend almost all of their time in combat during some games – and so the amount of times a common 'taunt' event is triggered will far exceed the amount of variations that are written, quickly resulting in repeated lines. Therefore, we get repeated playback not only of the recorded wave files themselves, but repetition of the same emotion and type of emotion that accompanies the same event throughout the duration of the game. Adding dynamics to the emotion of the character and developing some sort of an arc for these kinds of systems, based on evolving context, is a way of extending the believability and usefulness of these lines of dialogue, and also of being able to telegraph to the player much more about how the character *feels*. Dialogue variations should be treated in much the same way that sound design variations are treated but with even more attention to avoiding repetition – by treating the lines horizontally and vertically, with micro variations of the same type of line or phrase event, but also *contextual* variations across the timespan of the event. Diagonal design thinking about how these lines change over time, is especially worth tracking with very common dialogue events that support core game features.

Prototyping the performance aesthetics

I recommend looking at inspirational performances across a variety of media, and analysing the kinds of speech being used, especially the degrees to which psychological realism or vernacular speech is used. TV shows such as 'The Wire' are good examples of this, and the show was highly praised at the time for putting very authentic vernacular speech onscreen, with authenticity prioritised over conveying information.

Once you understand what the game direction and vision is from an aesthetic standpoint, you can start to apply these approaches to any scene or any dialogue situation between any number of characters. You may design your dialogue systems in the game to favour either one or the other method of performance, depending on the kind of information being communicated, you may well also decide to *cast* characters for informational roles differently from emotional roles. Again, making prototypes and benchmarks for testing out these kinds of performance types is essential in knowing what you want and what you don't want, as well as what works and what doesn't for your particular game. Think of these prototypes and benchmarks as style guides with which you can communicate the delivery, authenticity, clarity or ambiguity that you are looking from your performers.

Note

1 In this latter case of idea formulation in the moment, this is sometimes also referred to a psychological realism in acting terms, where the inner psychological state is the one being explored by the actor, and the effect that has on the way they speak the words, as well as the way their facial expressions change even when not speaking – the mode of acting, especially in terms of subtlety and nuance, or micro facial expressions and movements, has become far more prominent since the advent of the 'close-up' in cinema. In theatre, the emotional elements of the actor's face and body needed to be greatly exaggerated in order to be readable by every member of the audience in the theatre space, even those sitting at the back. This mode of acting did continue into much of the silent era of cinema, especially when there were mainly static camera positions, where the film audiences would essentially be watching a filmed theatrical experience onscreen. The methods of acting silently during this period, were also very much about this sense of exaggerated physical emotional performance, rather than small micro details we see and hear in cinema today.

25 Casting philosophies (auditions, recording, iteration)

Casting is one of the most important decisions you will make about your characters. If you can find an audition that so utterly and perfectly nails the character you are looking for, then you won't have to over-direct the actor in as intense a way as you would if you were having one actor play the parts of many different roles with many dialects and personalities. If you cast an actor who behaves and feels naturally like the character you are looking for in your game, they will naturally be able to perform as that character, and will also have many of the answers about how that character feels or would act in various situations. Often it is the timbre and cadence of a voice, or the familiarity with the specific vernacular speech that the character may have. As an example, if the game is in a real world setting such as East London, then actors with genuine knowledge and experience of the East End would be extremely useful in the expertise and authenticity they can bring to the performance – they will also be able to culturally advise, suggesting alternates for clunky lines that may have been written to supply the *information* needed in the moment, but that do not have the authenticity written into them. Very often a writer who is not from the culture does not have the ear for writing lines as they would be spoken. This is why the actor's *performance* is such a hugely important and collaborative part of video game development. It is the actor who is going to find and express the character onscreen. The actor is going to use the words written for them and combine them with the contexts given by the director. The characters are going to be found and understood, worked-through and ultimately materialised by the actor. When you have a situation in which an actor, who has already found the character, developed it, and understands their motivations, hopes, fears, desires and needs, and they are presented with dialogue lines that do not make sense for that character to say, then as a director or participant in those sessions you need to ensure that the actor continues to *own* the character and together you will need to make the necessary changes to those lines as part of that ongoing, trusting collaboration and exploration. I discourage writers at recording sessions for this reason, to me the written word is our jumping off point – the performance authored by the actor is sacred. This is the only source of truth on screen, so if we get an incredible performance, where the actor added a few words, the writers then re-transcribe what happened in the performance as text.

In recording sessions, I suggest making a point of having as few people in the room as possible. There certainly should be no 'tourists' when it comes to recording performances. Everyone in that room needs to be a part of the collaboration and creation of that performance together, and because everyone has an opinion, an extra person in a room can change and influence the relationships and the resulting performances in unpredictable and mostly negative ways just by being there. If they are not participating in the conversation and process of the performance, and if they have nothing to contribute, they should be asked, politely, to leave the room. Everyone who is present at a recording session needs to be there to support the actor in reaching the best performance.

Fairly often in games, writers will make the entire story and the entire game with words, so every moment that a character can possibly say something, they will have them say something. However, once the script is written, and the baton is passed to the actor and the voice director to bring that scene to life – we have the information (the script) so we need to focus on context, and emotions to guide us. If a character is going to the trouble to articulate and verbalise a thought, to *say something*, there needs to be a good reason for them to say something. Speaking is the act of rendering the character's thoughts into reality – we (the director and the actor) need to understand the motivations and contexts that are present for the character to do this. So just speaking for no reason or saying things that are already very obvious to the player, because they are already seeing them onscreen, always need to be reviewed and challenged.

> The actor has to understand enough to make it real from a deep place.
>
> (Lynch 2019)

Working with poor, or rushed, source material in a recording session is something that should always be avoided if possible, though even with the best intensions, it still happens. Just showing up to a recording session with lines that have been written at the last minute can be a recipe for a disastrously awkward session. A tendency I've seen in video game writers is to write how *they* speak – phrases with which the writer is familiar hearing and using themselves. Unless that is the target for the *character*, these kinds of culturally contextual, distinctly urban phrases do not apply to the world that the characters themselves are a part of. While not all writers are guilty of this, I have encountered a great deal of this kind of writing, particularly from those embedded primarily on game design teams, whose priority is on the game design side, rather than the characterisation and performance side. I would always recommend hiring writers who have specific experience in writing for characters in your particular genre, location or setting, as they will bring a huge amount of expertise.

Writing for games will usually need to be cleaned up, vetted and edited, and then most importantly, read aloud before getting anywhere near an actor. It seems like the most obvious thing to suggest but reading aloud what is written is absolutely essential if you expect an actor to actually say the lines out loud. The way we read sentences and words on a page in our heads is entirely different to how we speak and say those words out loud. There is physicality of the shape of the words in the mouth, the cadence, phrasing and breathing that needs to happen, and all of that needs to be built into the line if it is to be read out loud by a human being. The only way to edit and check for this kind of writing is to read it out loud, or better yet, get someone else, not as invested in the written dialogue line, to read the text out loud and listen for where they have trouble.

In the same way that poor source material for sound effects makes it difficult to produce a great end result, poor source material (writing) for voice affects the recording of strong dialogue performances. My preference is for the actor to take the reins as fully as they can during the performance and not be caught up in the committee discussions that can occur when there are too many 'owners' in the room from the game development side. Giving the actor and director the ownership of the performance is the best thing for the audience who listens to that performance. At worst, an improvised line misses, or obscures, a critical piece of information that is necessary for the player to understand what to do in the game – an easy fix with a pickup recording. I also think that there is genuine scope for a hybrid-role within teams that can work at the nexus between writers, directors and actors, to be a single point person who is both a lead writer who can vet the written content, and who also fully understands performance and direction and is able to step in and provide that direction too, with lots of experience in all of those categories. This way, lines will be commissioned, written and vetted with the end performance firmly in mind, and also the director can quickly and easily authorise any improvisational changes of the lines during the session, giving the actor the sense of freedom they often need in order to achieve a performance that is believable and emotionally engaging, and far beyond just the delivery of information to the player.

26 Let's do it again

Understanding and anticipating iterative cycles in dialogue development

In dialogue development, one common assumption in planning is to think that you will be recording your content only once, perhaps with a small last-minute pickup session, in order to get the perfect content. This dangerous self-belief ignores the decades of development experience that tells us that the game content will be constantly changing, constantly being adjusted and tweaked, and as the game evolves and changes, as the requirements and vision of the game morphs and mutates, then the dialogue will be constantly adjusted and re-written to accommodate the changes that are occurring in the game. Dialogue production is one of the slower areas to adapt to the fast, iterative methods of development and continual improvement that the other parts of the development team work with. Even if a story is locked, and the voice production is started, by getting the game experience onscreen with the real voices, the script and the story will always need to be adjusted and changed somewhat in order to better represent the experience that is developing. As this playable experience develops onscreen, there will appear problems and issues with perhaps locations, or the distances between locations, transitions between scenes that require that some characters and lines must be cut, some locations cut, new characters new lines added, and so on. The player in the end, will need to experience the *story* while playing the game, in such a way that they do not ever notice big cuts, rearranged material and missing elements from the *original* story and narrative, so the patching up and addition of bridging material in dialogue, will become necessary – as part of this iterative process. The 'script' is something of a 'live' entity, always being edited, continually going through revisions and changes – sometimes small changes, with the addition or removal of AI triggered categories for systemic dialogue (like a new bark category to support a new combat feature) – sometimes large changes, like the addition of entire maps or levels.

The problem is cyclical in that, the longer you wait to record (if you still think you can record this content only once), then the less time you have to ensure that everything can be done on time, at a high quality, and integrated to the same degree as all the other sound assets. Yet, if you record much too early, you will very likely have to re-record, and perhaps also re-cast several times.

Iteration is critical

Accommodating change into your thinking and into your dialogue creation process is critical. Planning on when to have scripts ready and recordable is also an act of almost superhuman co-ordination, faith and trust in your team. You cannot do this alone. There are several methods for doing this, but some of the most common are broken down into several major stages – such as temporary dialogue implementation, which lets iteration on the game design continue fairly rapidly until the moment when the game is deemed stable enough to record real actors. We'll look at a few of those stages now.

Text to Speech (TTS) file integration

Having a dialogue database and writer's tool that is able to generate TTS (Text To Speech) wave files in the pipeline is a very common approach that allows writers to generate their initial lines as files, then inside the game engine, scripters can get the correct triggering set up, making sure that these place-holder TTS dialogue files are playing at the correct time, and in the correct context. This version of game can be tested, even given to play testers so they can evaluate and give feedback on the overall flow and ensure the *information* is clear. The dialogue will usually sound horrible at this stage, although TTS speech is improving all the time. But the important element at this first step, is the right game engine triggering and the correct information in the line.

From there, once iterated enough, the next step is usually to increase the emotional performance of the spoken dialogue in the game, so a quick, cheap recording session is done, either with people from the game development team who are voicing the lines temporarily, or bringing in temporary actors to voice the characters for a demo or review. Again, this allows the dialogue placement and the lines themselves to be critiqued and challenged in the contexts of gameplay, by both the development team, and by play-testers. The more feedback can be taken on board the more the lines can be further refined. New TTS files may be generated *after* the reviews to address any feedback. These newly regenerated TTS files can then be either *re-recorded* again by the human temp actors, or, if satisfied with the content, a first real recording, with the real cast members, can be carried out.

What is outlined here is a very common process, and it makes sense to apply this iterative methodology to large and medium sized projects in which there are hundreds of thousands of lines of dialogue. However, if the project is much smaller, and perhaps only has a handful of lines, there is an opportunity to bring in the actual cast actors a lot earlier in this process and re-record with them many more times, as the sessions will be shorter and the content easier to get through and understand from a holistic viewpoint.

27 Rethinking dialogue production

Infinite alternatives

In terms of capturing the most believable performances, there are a great many ways that dialogue can be recorded. Recordings need not be limited to the solitary actor in a VO booth, or indeed limited to facial capture, or motion capture. These more industrialised and standardised processes have become common place through their use in large scale productions, in that they are efficient ways of getting through the amount of lines required in the amount of time allotted to a session, and in many ways this is the ideal way to make production sessions as efficient and lean as possible.

This lean approach is starting to be expanded away from the purely efficiency-driven, and to encompass more elements of creative freedom, invention and play on the part of the actors. We certainly need not be tied to these production-driven ideas in terms of how we think about inspiring and then capturing a certain kind of performance from an actor. Indeed, there is enormous opportunity to take the roads less travelled and to experiment with different performance and capture techniques that work specifically for your project's performance style. If you *begin* with defining the kind of performance you want, and then backwards-engineer the recording techniques and production pipelines around that performance, you will stand the best chance of authoring a unique process that fits your needs.

Some of the more interesting and adaptive techniques that have emerged in recent years, putting performance and authenticity first, rather than production efficiencies, have been in the realm of *ensemble* casting, direction and production. Geared towards getting a performance that feels realistic and convincing, ensemble cast recordings – beginning with rehearsals for table-reads, and assembling and recording scenes together in a generously sized recording studio environment – lean into the notion of giving the actors room to react to one another's performances. Once this approach has been decided, the recording methods and technologies need to adapt and *get out of the way.* With lavallière microphones attached to the actor's foreheads (for example, the DPA 4061) rather than the traditional *fixed* microphone position, actors can freely move around the space, and even physically interact with props or each other, as they perform the scenes. This is *not* motion capture, but voice-only recording, though it does take cues and inspiration from the kinds of authentic vocal performances, breathing and exertions that result from motion capture sessions. Voice and performance director Michael Csurics details this kind of unique approach in his GDC presentation from 2017: 'An experimental VO Production Post Mortem'[1] for the game 'Tacoma' (a sequel to the celebrated 'Gone Home'). In this talk he describes a bespoke approach to ensemble scheduling, shot lists and script preparation, as well as some choreography and studio layouts – this results in what Michael describes as 'organic realism', focussing on the actor's vocal performance, and not on the technical perfection of the recordings. So, for a walk and talk sequence Michael has the actors walk together around the studio as they talk. If someone is wounded and, on the ground, being attended to by another character, one actor is actually lying on the ground while the other actor attends to them. All the while, these physical performances are being captured by the head mounted microphones. An especially illuminating performance example was when one scene required a character to jump into another character's arms while the dialogue lines were being spoken. The results were exceptional, and if the same scene had been done in a fixed-mic studio with no physical movement, and perhaps with each actor recorded on different days, these scenes would have sounded obviously faked and not particularly convincing. As for the props, he suggests avoiding props that are acoustically reflective, and also those that create a lot of sound in the session – using proxy props like dumbbells for heavy objects the characters are catching or carrying during scenes also allows for good low-noise recordings. Another dimension of this is in avoiding *paper* scripts in favour of tablets that the actors can hold – this is to avoid the sound of paper pages being audible as the actors move and jump around.

The results of these performances and recordings are extremely convincing, and audiences feel that the characters are far more believable, giving the sense they are actually interacting with one another, which of course they are. The additional physical stresses on the voices that are caused by interaction with one another, and with props and objects, combined with the freedom to be physically anywhere in the room doing anything adds so much to the experience for the player – particularly in a game where the character performances are critical to the gameplay experience itself. These performances though, consisting only of audio, and no motion capture or facial capture data, are also to be used as the primary performance element that drives the animation department in authoring equivalent onscreen actions which match their vocal performances and physical stresses. This is very much the same way that animated features by Pixar begin their performance – with the *voice* of the actor only. In this sense, there is perhaps no better example of *leading with sound.*

As can be seen, figuring out what approach is needed for performance, is a major part of the pre-production and concept process. By developing dialogue performance benchmarks with an emphasis on authenticity and the required emotion, you are able to then author a pipeline and approach that will give the desired results for the entire game. But you first need to understand and know what you want, and this step, if not carried out early enough, can result in an approach to dialogue and performance that becomes driven by the technical needs of the game, and even by the production-centric needs of getting a certain number of lines done every session. When the more mechanical and technical production needs start to lead the dialogue process, the performance aspect will be something that simply gets in the way and will suffer a result.

If character performance is a big part of the game's identity and focus, then it becomes imperative to make the necessary prototypes, then benchmarks. Even earlier, developing style guides and examples of the kinds of voices and performances that are to be expected. Your game will likely have enough unique features and identity that it requires you and the team to find and define the unique priorities for capturing *exactly* the kinds of performance that make sense for your specific project.

This step is of course going to involve collaborating in both high- and low-level detail, with the many other departments that are working on the game. Discussing the many features, looking together at those feature requirements and putting those ideas onscreen as fast as possible, to learn about things that need to be tweaked is key. As a finished benchmark, or proof of concept, I would also strongly recommend casting and bringing in actors to enable your team to implement a final proof of concept that answers all possible questions. From there, you should have a clear recipe and budget to build out the rest of the game.

Of course, the most important aspect is that this all needs to be thought about and planned as early possible, in pre-production. Developing and exploring experimental techniques and pipelines takes a long time, and it can be hard to break established methods of recording that people are already used to, for example the same thing you did on your *last* project. There is available time to do this in pre-production, leading the process with the desired results first, and not waiting for the technology and production processes to *lead you*.

Note

1 Csurics 2019.

28 Leading with voice

Leveraging the spectacle of performance

Voice recording, capturing talent via motion capture, or any kind of performance capture – being the production and realisation of a story – is an incredibly exciting area for the team to once again be inspired and influenced by. Allowing everyone to see some elements of this process can be critical in shaping the work that the various disciplines and departments will carry out.

It is more than likely that the character you are casting and recording will have their look and animation style matched somewhat by the way the voice sounds when recorded. In many situations, actors are increasingly being 3D scanned to have their exact physical likeness used for the character they play in game. So, rather than *designing* the character onscreen via the traditional method of modelling and design, the physical casting of the actor replaces the design step – this method also brings the metaphorical puppeteer (actor) and the puppet (in game character model) closer together, merging the performance and model into a single entity on-screen.

It is vital to both open, and *keep* the doors open, for this kind of cross-disciplinary inspiration and interplay. Allowing for this kind of cross-influence to occur requires time, and time is the one thing that *every* game developer is always incredibly short on. With increased efficiency drives from production teams, whose very role it is to find and target anything perceived as an inefficiency in a workflow, there is less time available for disciplines to be able to openly figure out and understand what one another are working on. The increased importance of sharing and presenting the work being done on the voice recording side *early* is of utmost importance in leading with voice, especially when it comes to testing and validating new voice-driven performance capture approaches. Often times the most successful innovations in recording are ones that simultaneously increase the quality of a performance *and* create new production efficiencies as a by-product.

Similarly, any B-Roll footage of actors becoming and exploring the characters in the game can be of great inspiration to fans of the game post-release, and the more of this kind of footage can be gathered as part of the dialogue production, the more of the actual development arc of the character's performance can be shown and demonstrated – embracing the showcasing of the process, and especially highlighting the many different disciplines and people involved at each stage, is something that is not always evident in the majority of performance capture or voice recording footage that currently exists. Being able to show this whole process with a focus on the character, the story and the performance, rather than just a single focus on one discipline, be that cinematics, motion capture or audio, will serve to inspire even more collaborative thinking across the industry. I hope a more holistic and representational type of B-roll footage that shows all of those elements would depict a more realistic side of game development. I would encourage all future audio documentaries to consider the inclusion of viewpoints from *other* disciplines too, like game directors or performance capture experts, as is often done in the excellent SoundWorks Video collection series online. In these mini-documentaries, the focus remains on sound, but the interviews will invariably include the director's point of view – specifically talking about how important sound and music are to the overall film, or game in general.

In essence, voice performance, where needed in games, is an area that is especially opportune for re-invention and innovation. Every game project being unique, bringing new technologies and new approaches, also means that practically *every* game project's dialogue approach should be just as unique. Technology certainly plays a key role in performance and voice capture and playback, but it should not be fetishised or prioritised above the actual performance of the actor. Focus should always remain on the collaborative and human skills required to both communicate the vision to the actors, but also communication across disciplines to co-ordinate all the moving parts of the process, including, but not led by, the technology. This Herculean effort across multiple departments is the true story that we should be celebrating when showcasing the actor's performances onscreen.

Part V
The mix

Why do we need to mix?

Mixing is a fundamental, yet mostly under-estimated, under-budgeted and under-planned part of producing a video game audio track. This is one of the main reasons that it needs to be promoted to one of the major food-groups of video game sound development, if not *the* most important of the four.

As we have discussed throughout this book, for each of the other food-groups, one could quite conceivably have a game without dialogue, without music and very possibly even without sound effects, but as soon as you have any one of those elements, then you will absolutely still need a mix. Only a game with no sound of any kind would be un-requiring of a mix. So, in every sense, the mix is the element that concerns all other elements.

There is perhaps not a single conversation that I have with my teams (of any discipline) that does not in some way require some note or element of consideration about the mix of sound elements or the mix of a particular sub-element – because nearly every conversation about sound in games is about priority. Priority is an enormous topic, and represents a constantly changing, dynamic hierarchy of the audibility of sounds – it is also the simplest of questions: 'what is the most important thing?' Of course, answering this simple question is complex – driven by logic, and then unpicked again by the illogic of story, emotion and milestone reviews. But if you do not know the answer to this fundamental question, or you ask someone who *should* know but who doesn't, then you are potentially in deep trouble when it comes the mix.

Many varied approaches, attitudes, technologies and techniques to mixing prevail across different developers for various different reasons. Their mixing approaches are dictated by the kinds of games that they make and the kinds of audiences that their games have. This applies equally to the other three food-groups of sound, music and voice, however, the *mix* of these three food-groups together, the inter-relationship they have with one another and the priorities that they assume over one another, are all to be determined by the game being made. Another fundamental factor about the way developers choose to prioritise or de-prioritise their notions of mixing, is where the focus is in their game development culture in general – whether they are focussed on cinematic storytelling, or gameplay, or simulation systems – each of these approaches requires a completely different philosophy within the vast topic of mixing. In some cases the mixing is done almost entirely on the system level, by having passive mixing systems such as complex event-culling, side-chaining and auto-ducking set up and left to run with whatever content happens to play, without the need for a focussed final mixing session (as is the case of some continually updated game-as-service titles) – whereas big story-focused, linear triple-A titles will almost certainly require a thorough passthrough of the game's linear story towards the very end of post-production, and even detailed pre-mixing sessions per food-group, just as would be expected from a motion picture movie mix. Perhaps in some cases this last 'sanity check' mix takes place off-site from where the game is being developed, in a fully calibrated motion picture or TV mixing facility in a spatial surround format such as Dolby Atmos. The type and amount of hardware endpoints will also play a significant role, as will the amount of user-defined mix variability on each of those endpoints. So, the planning and priority that a team places on their mix will be a function of both the kind of game being created, the kind of audience expectations for that experience, the culture at the development studio (whether technology, financial or quality focussed) as well as the priority the team places on polish, detail and cross-platform user experience. But all this is just scratching the surface of the topic.

The idea that games somehow 'mix themselves' is one which I have encountered quite a few times, and it seems to be that the topic itself is often misunderstood, even sometimes among some very experienced practitioners. Most of the misunderstanding comes when considering differences between systemic passive methods of mixing, which in many cases are ways of automating some of the more basic building blocks of the mix (sidechaining, ducking, voice priority systems, and attenuation curves). However, little attention is paid to the areas in games that necessitate the *overriding* of these passive building block systems, and the *active systems* of mixing which usually become necessary to break all those convenient self-mixing rule-based technical systems. Yes, sometimes we really do need to hear that dialogue line from a distance at which it would not possibly be audible in reality, and yes, sometimes a single footstep sound does need to play louder than the rest, at a particularly tense story or gameplay moment... does that break the systems which you have built to mix the game? Yes. Does that mean that it is wrong that the player needs to hear those things? No. Does that mean you fight back against these creative ideas because your closed design doesn't allow this to happen? Not necessarily, and even the most stringent of systemic designs, can usually be very easily overridden to accommodate outliers. The idea that *context* will always come along and mess with your nicely balanced dialogue and music hierarchies and systems, is one that should always be carried with you when setting out to devise your mix approach. The fundamental practice of devising systems that are capable of being overridden is at the heart of almost all video games development practice. In an *entertainment driven* industry, the familiar resistance from systems engineers that 'No, we can't do that, this is not how the system we developed works' holds very little sway. Onscreen audience *experience* wins every time – static, unchangeable systems will always lose to this kind of creative driven approach. So, we are building systems to accommodate for the majority of cases, but always keeping in mind support for edge-cases and outliers that need to layer-in over the top of those systems, or temporarily disable those systems.

We cannot think or talk about music, dialogue or sound without talking about how they are mixed, whether within their own solitary food-group, or in relation to one another. The idea of thinking about the music or sound as single self-contained 'units' works only from a low-level production 'pre-mix' standpoint, and only up to a point. You can spend a lot of time pre-mixing each food-group, in dialogue for example, getting every line to play back at a consistent loudness level, across all lines and categories, however, the moment that these elements come together with sound and music, combined with the all important ingredient of 'context' that is supplied by the gameplay itself – *that* is when those food-groups generally, and quite occasionally the individual elements within them, need to be shaped and crafted further in the new reality of their *context*. This needs to be done so that quietly spoken dialogue lines stand out intelligibly over louder segments of gameplay, or that background music cues are appropriately impactful at the exact right moment in combat, and so on.

29 Mix essentials

Premixing

Premixing, or essentially 'mastering' at the food-group level, is an important step that needs to occur before any kind of final mix, or 'final contextualisation' occurs in the game. Having the dialogue, music, ambiences and sound effects all at relatively consistent levels within each food-group, is important to be able to even *prepare* the basic approaches of a final contextualisation. Having loudness bands within which assets in these broad elements exist is a standard way of achieving a premix. By levelling all the final recorded dialogue lines, taking into account whether the line is projected or whispered, or, in the case of music, finding a good general range for combat music, as well as a good range for the stillness of ambient music elements, we are able to set the stage for the final mix. This means that in the final contextualisation of all these elements, you will generally have everything in the right place before you begin at the overall hierarchical level, and not need to make radical adjustments to every single asset in the mix as you go – which would be a monumental waste of time during a final mix session. Being an interactive medium, it is also entirely possible that you will not be able to hear every single music cue or dialogue element during the finite time of a final master mix pass. And in that case, the assets that you missed, or the variations you didn't hear and the side-quests you didn't get time to check, can be somewhat relied upon to be at acceptable levels, even if not perfectly balanced, through the process of pre-mixing.

Loudness

Establishing and following an overall loudness level (a dBFS value expressed with the term LUFS – Loudness Units Full Scale) for the mix of the game is something that continues to be a major topic with many developers and publishers. If this approach is understood and attempted early enough, then the majority of problems associated with the game becoming too loud during development can be avoided. In establishing overall loudness levels for the game early on, you will also avoid the team perceiving a sudden drop in overall loudness when you do eventually enforce these loudness levels.

An understanding of overall output loudness goes hand in hand with working in a calibrated environment – meaning all the speakers you are using to monitor the sound of the game are outputting the same levels relative to your listening position – and are also equalised to have as transparent (or 'flat') a frequency response as possible. This is so the audio team can be confident that the speakers in every room in which critical development work is done are not colouring the sound you are hearing as you design and develop the game. The reference listening level in each room also needs to be correctly measured and calibrated in all the rooms that your sound designers and implementers use. If sound designers are left to their own devices, they naturally tend to set up their rooms differently, based on different *preferred* levels, and with personal preference for things like low-end. It is vitally important, from the earliest moments on a project, that everyone is using the same calibration methods, guidelines and techniques – and is aware of the correct recommended monitoring levels for their particular room volumetric.

Problems can very quickly begin to mount up in audio development environments that do not take a proactive and considered approach to calibration and consistency across their audio design and review rooms. For example, if one sound designer is working with their gain structure set up differently, and they are listening to their master output very quietly this means that, when they are implementing sounds into their maps, they could easily end up pushing the volumes of the sounds they are implementing *in the audio engine*. If they were monitoring at the correct output level – and placing and mixing sounds within the right tolerances – the sounds would be authored and balanced to the right degree. When several sound designers own or work on different maps, the inconsistency between them in terms of levels can be quite striking. This then fully necessitates a thorough and final levelling pass on all the different maps, in the same calibrated room, in order to get to a consistent loudness overall. This used to be even more of an issue when live in-game mix tuning was practically non-existent and when 'mixing' could only occur at the *asset* level – meaning the volumes of the wave files themselves were the only mix parameter that you had reasonable control over.

It can take a lot of time to figure out and understand loudness levels and reference level listening environments and how they feel for your team. Your approaches to loudness may need to change and shift several times over the course of a game development cycle, so *start early*, experiment, change, and you'll be ready and prepared by the time the game is almost shipped. It is absolutely paramount to learn how to calibrate your listening environments and understand the current industry standard recommended listening levels. There is good information freely available on how to do this, some of which is focussed on video games specifically, like the GANG IESD Mix Recommendations document version 3.02, published in 2015, which remains relevant and in line with current entertainment and broadcast standards.[1],[2],[3]

Final mixing or 'approved master mix'

Achieving an approved master mix is the process of spending dedicated time at the very end of the project, in a calibrated monitoring environment, specifically and solely to author all the final volume changes, attenuation changes, and any last-minute event separation for better perceptual sequencing. This time is solely used to get an overall contextual mix pass for the entire game, which becomes the 'sanctioned master mix'.

It is important to understand that the authoring of the final mix is not necessarily the 'end' of the mixing process, more like the beginning of the end – as this process, once complete, will then enable you to start to tweak many of the different user mix options that may be included in your options pages, elements such a dynamic range compression and make-up gain for different listening modes. It is important to discuss the sequencing of these big blocks of mixing and mastering time at the end of the project when you are planning your mixing schedules. It is vital to ascribe *time* to be able to focus exclusively on each stage of tweaking the mix before the game is shipped, and is out of your hands and in the hands of your audience.

The notion of the final mix is one that has been adopted from the post-production models of cinema sound, whereby the mix has traditionally been a dedicated and protected time in the production of the film's soundtrack. It is (theoretically at least) a time when all other visual changes have stopped, and all the pre-mixes and ADR is done, therefore mixing together all the *final* elements of the soundtrack into a cohesive whole before the film is exhibited theatrically. Though, for video games, the end of a project certainly looks quite different, and even though you may be focussed on making minor adjustments to lines of dialogue, or tweaking broad categories of music and panning, it doesn't protect you from having significant changes occur to the game while you are doing this. It is extremely prudent to have a few audio personnel resources available during a final mix period, so that they can jump in and fix bugs as they arise, or to play through and test areas of the game that have been changed – leaving you free to continue to focus on the mix. Whenever someone says that submitting some change list 'won't affect audio', you really cannot simply take their word for it, and you must always have someone familiar the sound, music and dialogue to go through and test those changes, ideally before they are submitted. There have been many occasions for me in the past 20 years where seemingly insignificant minor visual polishing has been added to the game during a final mix, that has completely broken the sound in that section of the game and necessitated quite drastic fixes or redesign. This kind thing certainly won't end anytime soon – a proactive communicative approach in tandem with the software and production finishing teams is highly recommended. Other than this, being prepared is the only thing you and your team can be.

Having talked about the importance of developing mixing systems, and mixing the content continually during production, we now shift to the importance and value that can be brought to production by planning and scheduling your final mixing phases. As already discussed, this is not to be thought of as the exact same kind of 'final mix' as would happen on a movie or Television show. In games, for final mixes (in my experience, and there are many species of final mix), ideally the content you arrive with is already fairly well mixed and in what could be called a shippable state at the point the final pass occurs. A final mix in game development is not deferring all the mix decisions to the end, it has a very different function. Broadly speaking it is a *sanity check* play-through of the entire experience in a calibrated environment. It is all about, ideally, making small tweaks, and pushing or pulling the *overall shape* of the narrative and gameplay experience. The process is one of ensuring that moments that need to be emphasised are emphasised to the right degree, and elements that need to be pulled back, are similarly brought under control and cleaned up. It is a last moment to look at the entire experience through the eyes and ears of the audience, to break all your usual working and thinking patterns, as well as making you more unreachable for answering minor issues and sitting in all the regularly scheduled meetings, and is *highly* recommended.

During the final play-through, and thanks to the amount of hierarchical bus control we now have through enriched game audio authoring tools, big *general* tweaks can be carried out that affect very broad groups of sound, like some subtle filtering or compression on *all dialogue* in the game, or perhaps all the dialogue of a specific character. One of the most important aspects in getting the most out of this end-phase of sound production is the addition of a re-recording mixer to your final mix team. A re-recording mixer, in video games, is someone whose role it is to sit with you and listen through the content, as a trusted set of fresh ears. Ideally, they have experience mixing entertainment products and bring their knowledge and expertise of all kinds of different media, such as film and TV to your team. You may also use the final mix to make some final sanity check loudness measurements, although you will also have been doing this throughout production, and hitting the targets expected, so loudness should already be very closely in line with the expected ranges and not present any big surprises.

Perceptual sequencing

There is a specific practical and philosophical approach to achieving a clear and readable mix in video games through a technique I refer to as *perceptual sequencing*, which is the process of separating clustered sound events triggered at the exact same moment into several distinct sounds. So, rather than relying on the timing of a single game event to trigger several things at once (dialogue, FX and music), thought can be given to the *sequence* that a character, or player, *perceives* the sounds associated with the event. This approach allows these triggers to be separated in various ways, depending on the event, for example, if there is a huge explosion and we have a bad mix situation whereby the sound of the explosion triggers, *and* immediately triggers a dialogue reaction to the explosion, *as well as* triggering a music cue to accompany the explosion. The thinking we would apply to break apart these elements into a perceptual sequence of events, would be as follows...

1   explosion sound effect plays in-sync with the visual event onscreen (in line with supporting 'objective' physics-based 'reality');
2   dialogue response then plays a few seconds after the event (representing an intellectual or visceral reaction depending on character POV), this fits with the psychological reality of a delayed reaction to a 'shock';
3   music cue plays *after* the dialogue or comes in *just* underneath it (the emotional reaction and narrative significance of what happened) giving the audience the sense of the *deeper* emotional and visceral reaction to the explosion – especially if it is a particularly *meaningful* explosion.

A further focus on perceptual sequencing of events is entirely recommended during the final mix play-through – indeed it may be easier to identify these opportunities in the final mix – anywhere we lose the impact of the sound, lose the clarity of the dialogue, and lose the emotion of the music because all these elements are fighting for bandwidth and dominance at the same temporal moment. For those craving a more memorable analogy, this kind of event separation is like taking white light and splitting it into constituent colours using a prism. This is relatively easy to do at this final stage because these kinds of delays can usually be added to separate sound events in-engine, as the game still runs, without the need to rebuild the content entirely and listen again.

Anchoring the mix

Finding the central sound ingredient around which to *anchor* a mix is a fundamental approach that needs to be fully understood and discovered ahead of time. The anchor will be the primary sound group around which all other sounds are balanced and attenuated against. Very often, in narrative story driven games, this will be the dialogue. In shooters, it would be the weapons. Ensuring these levels sit correctly, front and centre in the mix, would often be the first thing that you would do on day one of a final mix. Bringing up the anchor levels (already premixed of course) on the main bus group fader, so that the levels sit where you have determined for the experience of the player is almost always the first thing that needs to be set and considered. This will give you the feel for the entire mix. Once done, all other elements can be brought in and built up around that central element, in *support* of that anchor. So, for example, background ambience, music score and interface sounds, will all be brought up to levels that relate well to that main anchor element, but that do not overwhelm or swamp it.

If dialogue is not present in the game, then another central anchor element will need to be found – in games like 'Journey', 'Beat Sabre' or 'Sayonara Wild Hearts', the music is the clear anchoring element within the mix, around which all else is balanced. Whereas a game like 'Limbo', whose score is not continual enough to become an anchoring element, has the character *Foley* as the primary element around which the experience is mixed around.

Understanding the anchoring element allows you to find the *entry point* into your overall mix and allows you the opportunity to continually reference and check that the anchor point is still sitting correctly throughout the whole experience. Not only this, but understanding what this is *early* enough in development, will allow you to build more detailed systems, prioritise feedback and also ensure that whatever the central anchor point is has the most thought, variation, complexity and dynamism built into it. This anchoring element of the soundtrack is essentially the thing that the audience will hear the most of, expect the most *feedback* from, and will likely be the most prominent element in design conversations, as well as the most dynamic element in terms of communicating emotion or change of mood over *time*. Ideally, the anchor point, should not be something that you 'find out about' on the first day of the final master mix pass – it should be something that you already understand well, and have worked on from the beginning of development. A major part of your effort and vision should be applied to this central element of the game – for instance, the complex Foley system that was developed for the game 'INSIDE', was also the central element around which the entire game was mixed, as well being the most important element of feedback in the platforming experience.

Notes

1 'Recommendation ITU-R BS.1770–3'. *International Telecommunication Union, Radio Communication Study Group,* www.itu.int/dms_pubrec/itu-r/rec/bs/R-REC-BS.1770-3-201208-S!PDF-E.pdf. Accessed 1 Aug. 2020. This broadcast document that has been widely adopted by the video games industry as the standard loudness -24LUFS per half hour of gameplay.
2 'ATSC Recommended Practice: Techniques for Establishing and Maintaining Audio Loudness for Digital Television (A/85:2013).' *Advanced Television Systems Committee, Inc.,* ATSC, www.atsc.org/wp-content/uploads/2015/03/Techniques-for-establishing-and-maintaining-audio-loudness-1.pdf. Accessed 12 Mar. 2020. Room volumes and reference listening levels are established based on the volumetric dimensions in cubic feet of the listening environment. For home entertainment mixing, a usual reference level is set at 79dB SPL.
3 'GANG IESD Mix Recommendations.' Game Audio Network Guild, GANG IESD, www.audiogang.org/wp-content/uploads/2015/04/IESD-Mix-Ref-Levels-v03.02.pdf. Accessed 11 Mar. 2020. The GANG IESD loudness recommendations document for video games, both console and mobile.

30 Philosophy of the mix

Narrative dynamics (pushing, pulling, shaping)

Once the anchoring element has been established and taken its place in the mix, the next major element to consider is that of finding the overall dynamic *shape* of the experience – this is the fundamental backbone of the mix and refers back to our overall tension curves from the sound chapter. This is the process of being able to understand where the tension and release points are, as well as where the *reward* and celebration moments are in the experience for the player. This will become the overall shape of the experience for the audience, and using the mix to articulate and emphasise this shape is the goal. Every small detailed adjustment that you might end up focussing on, sometimes for hours, in a mixing session, will need to *serve* this overall experiential shape in a meaningful way.

In terms of shape, point of view is an extremely important aspect that must be also be talked about during the mix, just as we have talked about the subject in terms of sound design, voice and music composition or supervision – the subjective point of view of characters, or the player, is also one of our main guides during the mix. When we listen to the sound in a game, particularly a narrative driven title, we are putting onscreen what the player hears, and *prioritises*, through a particular character's 'ears', through their point of view (POV). This POV is precisely how they are able to hear things that, objectively, could be inaudible – or that another character with a different point-of-view wouldn't deem important enough to notice. The POV in a mix tells us what the character cares the most about, what they notice, and reflects how their internal mental state affects what they hear, and how they hear it. It all comes back to the fundamental idea of what is the most important thing to the character, or the player's role-play character, at that moment. We are attempting to replicate what a very specific human brain is hearing, and in some cases what they imagine that they hear. Another lens we can bring into play here are our three audiences, the first two being the most important: the player, and the spectator. We need to make sure first and foremost that the player has all the audible information they need to play the game, and secondly that this information is balanced in a way that isn't over-the-top in terms of presentation for the spectator.

This entire approach may also be thought of as a way of dynamically focussing the ear of the player, in and out on various elements in the game, as the perception and importance of various sounds, or categories of sound, changes according to the dynamic forces of gameplay and story. We need to be continually asking and most importantly *answering* the question 'what is the most important thing?'

As mentioned, a useful toolset we can refer back to here are the intensity and dynamics curves that have been created for the understanding of the dynamics of each map, feature (in the case of combat or exploration gameplay loops etc.), or moment, in the case of cinematics. Although, from experience, these documents will often have become outdated once the game reaches this final stage and becomes very well realised on screen. Like all documentation, the intensity curves are a guide and starting point for the teams that are implementing the work, and also a guide for the director to be able to understand and answer questions about the minutiae of the experience as it is being created by the team. They are a method of getting the desired intentions onscreen, and once the experience arrives on screen, it is important to leave behind the intensity curves and to attend to the shape of the game onscreen. Once reaching the upper limits of the L3 level of quality, the game itself becomes the single point of truth.

The overall 'shape', meaning the dynamics and the focus of the experience, may have evolved quite a lot since the implementation step, and thus will have taken on a new overall shape – in most cases this won't be enormously different from the shape and intentions of the dynamics curves. Nevertheless, it can be prudent to have these dynamics curves as a reference point, but also to look at and talk about the original intentions for the shape of the dynamics onscreen. The role of a re-recording mixer, the fresh pair of ears to accompany you during the mix of the game, is invaluable in this sense too, because they will be looking specifically to *understand* the dynamic shape and tone of the game, and will be doing this through a combination of observing what is onscreen, and asking questions about what the intentions are if something is unclear – just as they would when they sit with a movie director in the final mix of a motion picture. They will also be looking to untangle the three food-groups of voice, music and sound effects from one another in order to push and pull those broad stems in terms of prominence and focus. This is so that each important element comes through to the audience with *clarity* and also with a degree of finesse and polish that essentially means the audience isn't *noticing* the mix decisions that are occurring. In other words, making sure the audience does not *hear* things being turned up or down continually throughout the mix, and that the experience is a fluid and subtle refocusing of sound elements.

So, the shape of the mix at this final stage could be said to be the final expression of the overall dynamics and intensity of the game. This is a moment at which it is just as important to listen to what the game is telling you – just as much as it is about imposing your creative will and decision making over the various ingredients of the soundtrack. If a moment *feels* like it needs to be more intense, or clearer, then this is the moment to emphasise that. Perhaps it is a case of pushing the excitement of the *driving* elements in the score at a particular denouement. Perhaps there are more subtle moments where the audience needs to lean in and be attentive to stillness – you may need to be similarly bold in terms of dropping levels and drawing the audience in closer to the experience.

Perhaps one of the most useful ways that we can think about the mix is in terms of what moments we need to draw the player *into* the screen, the more intimate moments where we want the player to 'lean in' and open their eyes and ears wide, versus the moments where we want the player to be pushed back into their seat, to grip the controller and *engage* in the action onscreen. This continual dynamic of drawing the audience in, then pushing them back in their seats, is one that I often consider when listening back to the final version of a game on a big screen mix stage. For some reason, the very act and *experience* of mixing a game on a large screen, in a larger room than I am used to working in, instantly and firmly re-frames the game into the category of *entertainment spectacle.* At this stage, I am definitely no longer thinking at all about software development. Here you begin to really understand what you are making, and can experience it and craft it, from that entertainment perspective.

Such a shift in location and mindset, if possible, at this precise endpoint in the creative audio process, is one of the most important elements of transforming your mindset from software development, to entertainment. Getting the game off-site and into a place where you are surrounded by other creatives who mix and craft entertainment experiences all year long, immerses *you* into that world, among those people, and into that mindset. Through this environmental change, you will also be away from the *culture* and mindset of bugs, programmers, software and daily scrums, and you will be immersed instead, in the world of entertainment and spectacle.

This mental shift can be extremely positive for your focus on the most important things, and should not be underestimated as a factor in the intentions of what you do when you are spending time to specifically focus on crafting those final dynamics and the final shape of the mix of the game. Given these new surroundings, it is much more likely that you will end up with something that *feels like* a piece of cinematic or entertainment spectacle. You will pick up a lot of the language that is used and be able to start to think and talk about elements of the soundtrack in much more broad creative and craft oriented terminology. This is certainly not to say that motion picture mix environments are the *only* places you could mix a game, sometimes this is not appropriate at all, depending on the kind of game being made. The important thing is getting into a calibrated environment, as well as a secluded enough place to focus – away from the general chaos and stress of the rest of the team as they attempt to kill the final bugs and stabilise the build. I would highly recommend, whenever you can, to shift your mindset and craft approach *away* from software development, and lean heavily into the entertainment industry's craft, storytelling, POV and emotion-based approach, especially in the final polish phase, so that you can be influenced appropriately to push and pull the experience you are putting on screen *before* it reaches the audience.

No favourites in the mix

In the end, the audience will experience the version of the game that has been passed through this final mixing process, one that is done in order to create a final sanctioned version of the game for the audience. It is vitally important to understand that, as a *result* of this mixing process, there may well be a lot of detailed work done on the music side, or the Foley and SFX side, and the ambience side, that is for the most part, no longer audible to the player 100% of the time.

No matter how much work and time has been spent on each of those separate elements by how ever many teams of talented people, no matter what amount of money has been expended on each element, the *most important aspect of the mixing process* is that the audience is able to hear with clarity *what they need to* in order to understand, on a moment to moment basis, the experience as a piece of interactive entertainment.

If that means turning down music cues to get out of the way for the critical dialogue at a certain specific moment, then the decision is the right one. There is no decision that is the wrong one when you are putting the player and their emotional entertainment experience *first*.

I would strongly encourage, in whatever role you have as a director, or leader of the mix, not to have 'owners' or authors of any of the three main food-groups of voice, music and sound present at the final mix session. They will try to be there. You must say no. Their influence on the mix stage will be coloured to best serve their own food-group, rather than the game itself as an overall experience and story. This is why, when you are present at a final mix, you need either to be the person who is able to make those decisions in as objective a way as possible, or you need to hire an objective re-recording mixer to help you do this.

Remember also that any 'owner' of, or invested contributor in, any of those three food-groups will have only been hearing their *version* of the game mix for the entirety of development, one heavily skewed towards their food-group. The decisions that you make in the final mix will need to be fresh decisions that take into account the presence of the final versions of all the other food-groups together.

It is likely that the presence of any of these food-group owners will result in disappointment and tension, making the task of mixing far less pleasant and enjoyable. If you find the mix becoming a matter of political appeasement, rather than that of crafting the emotional shape of the entertainment experience for the player, then you'll need to address the issue quickly. As always, these are my own notes, based on experience, and of course you should feel entirely free to put whoever you *need* in that final decision-making process.

Every game is different, every team is different and every culture is different, so it should of course be down to whatever works best and is the most comfortable for you in the end – if a game is music centric, with a music mix as the anchor point, then of course having the composer in that final mix makes perfect sense.

In an ideal world, you will be spoiled for choice in terms of what has the emphasis in any particular mix moment – between world class music, incredible dialogue performances, as well as beautiful and immersive sound design and ambiences. However, you cannot make everything of equal priority, and the best way to feature the best content for each moment, is to author a mix that is as dynamic as possible. To do this, you will need to use many different techniques and features of non-linear mixing.

31 Some defining terminology and features of non-linear mixing

Though it requires some slightly more technical categorisation, we will explore and outline some of the most common concepts of non-linear mixing, but we'll do this from quite a high-level without touching on too many specific technologies or tools.

We will also define and explore some use-cases for the following categories, and we will consider both active (non-systemic) and passive (systemic) interactive mixing techniques. A working understanding of the differences and nuances between these elements, and how they all interrelate, is essential in order to be versant in both the creative, technical and collaborative elements available to you in the mix. Mixing any game could consist of a combination of some or all of these techniques, and they can all be used in conjunction with one another for various features, modes or types of presentational moments in-game.

Busses

A bus is simply a way to organise sounds into categories by assigning and grouping them to a single channel (a bus) which can then be used to collectively control all of the sounds that are assigned to it. Busses are hierarchical in video game mixing, and 'child' busses inherit the values assigned to 'parent' busses above them, unless they are overridden. A good example is if we have a subcategory of dialogue for all of the NPC (Non-Player Character) bark and attack dialogue. Every single one of those individual sounds will be assigned to the VO_NPC_Barks bus. This bus in turn is the *child* of a bus called VO_NPC, and that bus is itself a child of a bus called VO.

As can be seen, given this structure of inheritance, if we were to adjust the volume level of the fader on the VO bus, all the VO in the entire game would be modified accordingly. However, if we *only* wish to reduce the volume level of the NPC VO, we would instead adjust the volume levels at the NPC_VO bus location in the hierarchy. Again, if we need even more precision, and just want to add a high pass filter to the NPC's casual overheard background chatter, we would add the effect to the VO_NPC_Overheards bus – and this action would only filter and affect those dialogue lines that are assigned to it.

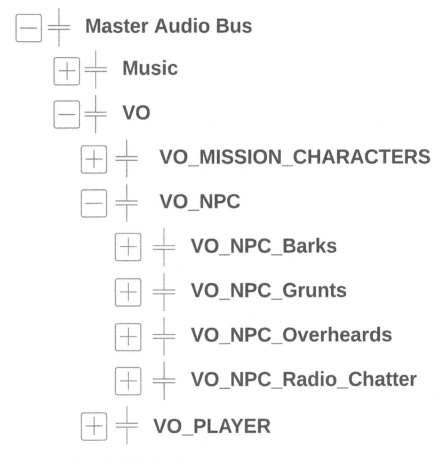

Figure 31.1 Example Wwise Bus Structure

These bus structures can be created and nested in any way you like, and you can add as many sub busses as you like to get more detailed in terms of the categories of sounds and their inheritance. The bigger a project, the more likely the game is going to have a very large and complex bus hierarchy. It is also likely that a large project is going to make use of several bus related structures and concepts like auxiliary (or aux) sends as well as mix states and sidechaining.

Auxiliary, or 'aux' busses and sends

Having your sounds broken down into bus categories is the first step in organising the priority and control structure of the sound in the game. Another important element of this kind of structure, is the ability to choose to 'send', or duplicate, a signal, or group of signals, to another bus with different output values and settings, or even perhaps to effects channels. The busses that receive these kinds of signals are a sub-species of bus called the 'auxiliary bus'.

The most common use-case for an auxiliary bus is if you require certain sounds to hit an environmental reverb effect. You will usually set up the instance of that reverb and the effect's properties in one place, on a single auxiliary bus, usually named something like 'Generic_Exterior_Reverb'. Keeping the environmental reverb in one place means that the properties, such as room size and EQ, of the overall effect can be tuned and tweaked in one place, as well as the balance of the amount of original (dry) signal and the amount of reverb (wet) signals that will be heard. Once that is set up, the signal from any other regular bus, or any game object that you wish to send to that reverb, can be achieved by choosing the amount of signal that is sent to that Generic_Exterior_Reverb auxiliary bus.

Another example of using auxiliary buses is if you want to dynamically change the kinds of speaker output routing for a set of sounds. Auxiliary busses are great for thinking about splitting, duplicating or siphoning off signals into other parts of the bus structure, and even to different endpoints. They can come in extremely useful when thinking about how to avoid copying or recreating large actor-mixer type game object hierarchies to handle slightly different playback instances like panning and effects.

State-based (or mixer snapshot) mixing

State based (sometimes referred to as 'snapshot' based) mixing is a method of setting specific values (not just volume, but any filter or effect values) for whole sets of buses and objects at specific moments in a game. A snapshot, or state, could be thought of as a *preset* for different values. If we have a pause menu for example, we may wish to install a state that sets the bus or voice volume levels for certain groups of sounds, like the in-game dialogue, or the in-game physics sounds, to -96dB (silence), and then to pause those sounds. This is done so that these categories of sounds are no longer audible when the menu (and state) is initiated. We will then of course, return to the 'default' or 'default in-game' mixer state when the menu is unpaused (at which point the values are re-set back to 0dB, or whatever their original values were) and we can return to hearing the in-game sounds routed through those busses once again.

Mixer states can be also be applied to narrative events, either specific dramatic or story moments in specific maps, for example by applying each beat or checkpoint in the map a specifically named snapshot, and then installing that when the beat is initiated, or the checkpoint is restored – for example 'Jungle 01-Plane Crash' and then 'Jungle 02-Campfire'. These two states could then be tweaked so that sound values of busses can be slightly altered between those two states. The amount of control offered over the audio doesn't end there, as practically any value can be changed or set by the installation of a state. The RTPC (Real Time Parameter Control) value for the amount of wind in the system could be altered, as well as changing other states such as time of day. Of course, many different state groups and *states* can be active at the same time, so managing and tracking what states are installed can become challenging in terms of organising and making sure states are uninstalled or returned to defaults. One of the other essential elements to consider is the amount of time, and the type of curve over time, that the states need to transition, and this can be set as a 'transition time'. For example, we could set ten seconds to crossfade from the values of the 'Jungle 01-Plane Crash' to the 'Jungle 02-Campfire'. This way, when the state change is initiated, all the values will slowly change from their current values to the new target values, over the specified time of ten seconds, using the specified fade curve.

The different modes in games, for instance the combat system, could be broken down into several states within a combat state group, like 'pre-combat', where we want to have a bit more stillness, tension and foreboding, followed by the different kinds of combat that may be triggered, such as 'combat stealth', 'combat assault', etc. Each of these states could transition from one to the other using customised timing and transitions. States can carry a whole range of actions applying to more than just the mix, those same states could also be used to drive changes in the music system, by triggering different music layers. Finally, a 'combat success' or 'failure' state could be called to signal the outcome of the combat, and can again trigger music cues, as well as setting customised bus values, perhaps adding some muted low pass filtering to all the in game ambience sounds, as well as pushing up the auxiliary send to the in-game reverbs, to give a stylised 'concussion' effect of being knocked out of the game.

Managing and understanding mixer states can become quite intensive, and often requires the game audio engine to have a separate mixing panel or interface available so that the different bus and fader values, as well as the states being installed can all easily be viewed, navigated and tuned when necessary. I also find it useful to display the currently installed mixer states and state groups onto the game onscreen as we play and tune it, using some debug display text – this way we can see and monitor exactly what states are active, as we mix.

Side chaining

Side chaining is a way of setting up automated volume, eq or filter changes across one or more busses, by driving the volume level of one group of sounds from the meter level of another group of sounds. By far the most common use for side chaining, in story driven, or dialogue-centric titles, where side chaining is dynamically set up to read the volume levels that are coming through the master *main character* VO bus, and using that signal information to duck out any other background dialogue that might be playing at the same time, but which is not as important, such as NPC character buses. The great thing about setting up side chaining, is that once it is done, this will continue to be applied to every audio signal that passes through those busses, so it becomes a very powerful systemic way of prioritising specific categories of sound in the mix. As mentioned, not only do you have influence over the volume level reduction of the target sounds, but also control over filtering, pitch (if need be) as well as the potential to only carve out *specific* frequencies in the target sound using an EQ that is driven by the side chain.

Ducking

Ducking is a more primitive and significantly less processor intensive way of doing something similar to side chaining, however, it is much less nuanced, and rather than reading the input volume in real time and applying the appropriate attenuations to the target bus, ducking treats source buses as binary on off switches. So, if any kind of signal is detected coming through a bus, of any volume, then it will trigger the ducking effect on the target – which is usually specified by the amount of dB with which to reduce the target bus by. So, if a sound plays through the main character VO bus, and we have set up ducking to happen on the music bus, then as soon as the signal is detected going through the main VO bus, then the music bus will start being ducked. Then, whenever that signal stops the ducking attenuation will cease being applied. You can usually specify a fade up and down time to the ducking effect in most audio engines, however, it can be a rather obvious and audible way of setting up an automated mixing system, particularly when you have much more transparency when using side chaining.

Distance-based culling based on audible fall-off (attenuation curves)

Attenuation curves, or distance volume fall-off curves, are another method of mixing a game by using the 3D positions of the sounds in the game, and their distance from the listener, and applying the volume, filter and reverb attenuations that occur as those sounds become closer or become more distant. By thinking about attenuation in 'groups', certain types of sounds (grouped in terms of 'attenuation values') could be faded out and made inaudible much sooner than the others. If sounds need to remain audible, even when they are in the distance, we could also be said to be assigning these sounds a *higher priority* in the 3D mixing field. These kinds of distance-based sound prioritisations are often used in conjunction with all of the other mixing methods mentioned above, as a way to further automate mixing, and enforce priorities.

HDR (High Dynamic Range) – moving window dynamic range

This runtime system of dynamic sound voice prioritisation is based on a scale of dB SPL (Sound Pressure Level) values assigned to each sound event being triggered, was co-invented by several members of the sound team at D.I.C.E. in Sweden and it continues to be a significant auto-mixing approach for the culling of sounds throughout the industry, especially since a version of this technique was implemented by Audiokinetic in their Wwise middleware engine.

The principle is simply a system that is continually checking what sound it is possible for the player to hear, in advance of even playing the sound, and then either playing or discarding sounds that fit or don't fit into that dB window's range of sound. The 'window' moves up or down depending on the value of the loudest sounds that are being played at any one time and the range of the sounds audible in the window can be adjusted and tuned to achieve the desired effect. If a very loud explosion is playing right next to the player's position, then much quieter sounds like footsteps that are triggered at the same time, will simply get ignored and not be played – this is because it is arguably impossible to hear those quiet sounds when a louder sound is present. When the louder sounds have gone, the footsteps can be played once again. The system results in a very clean mix, with a lot of detail present when there needs to be – i.e. in quieter more intimate or stealthy moments – as well as producing a voice-count friendly mix, especially when the action is loud and intense. This culling of triggered sounds also has the advantage of massively reducing the amount of sound voices that are being used, by pre-calculating if a sound will be audible or not, and not playing anything that is not audible. Another advantage to this system is that the question of 'what is the most important thing' is basically deferred to the SPL dB hierarchy of sounds we would physically expect to be able to hear. Put simply, louder sounds are more important than quieter sounds. This kind of prioritisation based on loudness is also arguably one of the down-sides of running a system like HDR exclusively, because at some point in the game narrative, you will need to override some of those 'real-world' values in order to play a narratively important, but quiet, sound in the game that is audible no matter what else is happening. In those instances, you might author a specific, unique asset, and 'fake' the assigned dB SPL value, so that the system can be tricked into always playing that sound. Many developers run HDR systems that are overridable and customizable beyond simply letting the system run on static SPL values alone.

Voice priorities and event pre-culling

In a similar approach to HDR, there also exist many custom and proprietary ways of 'pre-culling' sound events *before* they are triggered to play. This means that there is a voice management system running at the *game engine* level that determines whether or not to even attempt to trigger a sound before it reaches the audio engine and hits all the other prioritisation systems that may be running audio engine-side for further sound prioritisation based on either metering, the distance from the listener, or the audible dB ranges of sounds as well as any side-chaining that occurs once a sound has been played through a particular bus.

Pre-culling is becoming more of a desirable step in terms of managing the amount of voices that it is possible to simultaneously trigger and manage at runtime in the audio engine itself. In Real-Time Strategy (RTS) games for example, the amount of sounds that are triggered during a huge battle scene when the camera is close up and zoomed right into the action, is based on the triggering of sound events from a wide variety of onscreen sources such as animations, gameplay events and other logic systems such as VO grunt and bark systems. However, when the camera is zoomed out further and further away from those events, all the player sees is a large crowd of soldiers on a battlefield, and at this stage, even though all those events that are now out of range and inaudible, they may still be triggering and taking up a sound voice. But with a voice management system, these events are able to be stopped from triggering because they are pre-culled by suitable distance from the camera or listener value. Instead, then, the crowds are treated by the game engine as a single large entity, and it is this 'group entity' which now has a sound triggered on it, this could be a single ambient walla group sound for the large battle, or a charge, retreat or defeat – as well as some large scale group Foley and battle sounds on another sound layer, depending on context. So, instead of thousands of sounds being triggered and managed by the audio engine using virtual voices, we now simply have a small group of three or four sound layers playing on that huge group of people fighting. With a lot of finesse and forethought for the different perspectives and crossfading of content, the system can be designed and implemented in such a way as to match what the player sees, and make the act of quickly zooming in and out from the free camera *appear* as though all sounds are always playing all the time. Another advantage of this kind of grouping of sounds, or treating sounds at LOD (Level of Detail) in terms of grouping into single crowd sounds, is that it is not very convincing to make something *sound* like a crowd when it is made from thousands of individually triggered events – these sound triggers may also become extremely dependent on the frame rate at which the game is running. This kind of thing can sound extremely programmatic, repetitive, phased and mechanical and the individual sounds do not diffuse and propagate with one another in the way that they do in real air – and this is something that our ears are very well trained to detect. So, having an actual recording of a distant group of walla or Foley, will always sound far more convincing and believable than the version made up of thousands of individual short sounds re-triggered over and over again by a computer system. Beyond RTS games with free moving cameras, this pre-cull and LOD approach is used quite often in many triple-A and even mobile games, as it dramatically reduces the amount of voices, decoding and mixing that the CPU needs to handle for vast amounts of sound events implied onscreen.

32 Mix consistency

Panning and centre-channel consistency

The surround mix in almost every game you listen to will have some extremely varied approaches, and usually in some fundamental ways one might not expect. In motion picture mixes, there persists a very consistent approach across almost every movie when it comes to panning of dialogue and Foley. This consistent approach is a centre-channel focussed approach, simply meaning that anything that is *onscreen* will be panned through and positioned in the centre channel – this includes all sounds in the diegesis. This centre-channel magnetism is a method of attaching sound *to the screen* in front of the audience – indeed this is the audience's focal point throughout the entire movie. If something moves or pans offscreen, panning occasionally wanders slightly from the centre position, but not in an extreme way into left or right channels that distracts the audience from the screen (in cinemas, speakers are placed extremely widely apart and panning to left or right means the sound can jump dramatically *off* the screen). This consistent screen-anchored theatrical approach, more recently, especially in animated film and with the advent of Dolby Atmos in cinemas, has started to embrace and drift, at particular moments in the film, some more dramatic spectacle-centric panning approaches to sound sources away from these more conventional cinema mixes.

However, in games, the *approach* to panning and to what does or does not live in, or pass through the centre channel, is entirely inconsistent, and mostly invented by the sound team for each project.

One of the most common, and in my opinion *poor* panning choices in 3D action video games, is to exclude all diegetic sound, except dialogue, from the centre channel. In the early days of 5.1 video game panning, *before* any sophisticated run-time mix prioritisation (like side chaining) was available, I recall much discussion around this approach. The case for excluding diegetic sound from the centre was that the dialogue needed to be very clear, and was essentially given its own speaker, so it could always be exclusively clear and not compete for bandwidth from any other sounds in this single channel. This reasoning didn't really hold water when it came to down-mixing. This was essentially a way to defer and covert what were really mixing and clarity decisions into the panning decisions. Different degrees of this approach continue today, and while it may work fairly well for 5.1 home entertainment speaker arrays or sound-bars, where the L-R channels are very close to either side of the screen, it doesn't account for the dynamic array of endpoints we have in games today. It also fails to take into account that whenever diegetic sound effects in 3D are panned *onto* the screen, essentially whatever the player moves the camera to look at their source position, being a blend of only Left and Right speaker channels misses out the centre-channel and thus leaving a dead spot in the 3D image at the centre of the screen, so the feeling of presence of those sounds in the diegesis is completely lost. The lack of presence onscreen created by this approach feels extremely unnatural, and does not reflect the successful approaches of other popular entertainment media like film or TV that our *audiences* will be used to.

My preference and recommendation for a panning approach is to spend some time to analyse and examine carefully how movie and TV surround mixes (particularly in the *genre* of game that you may be creating) treat and incorporate the centre channel. Being the only channel that is actually anchored to the what we see, it becomes the speaker with the most importance and prominence in helping the sound and the visuals gel together. It is no less than *the diegetic channel.*

Hearing onscreen elements like rockfalls in front of the audience onscreen *come* audibly from that exact location is essential in achieving a solid diegetic audio-visual contract with the content. It is about achieving a parity with more established entertainment panning schemes who have developed this approach so that the sound onscreen is believable, nuanced and connected to the world. You may have a lot of sound to contend with in the centre channel, but this should only sharpen your approaches and concern with the prior-itisation of sound in your games.

Of course, in games, we can entirely expect our audiences to be more familiar with navigating and exploring 3D worlds and understanding the presence of spatial elements of gameplay events *off-screen.* In this sense, using sound more energetically in the surrounds and overheads in our mixes is cer-tainly an area we can explore further than in cinema. However, to do this to the exclusion of the *centre channel*, arguably the most important spatial anchor to the screen itself, and to the visual world of the game itself, feels like a mistake – and a left-over from the far less sophisticated days of primitive game mixing and panning.

(Over) use of LFE channel

LFE is a similar element to centre channel in terms of having picked up some very inconsistent bad habits over the years. The rather extreme approach, prevalent in a few games around 2001 to 2006, seemed to be that the LFE channel should be in *constant* use for all low frequency sound in the entire game. This was when games were first able to use the 5.1 surround format, and content creators probably felt that this extra 'effect' channel had to be used to its maximum potential. The thing that appeared not to be understood was the distinction between LFE and crossover Sub – that LFE is a discreet channel that is able to produce a very spectacular additional low frequency effect – and that Sub, which can be set-up however it is preferred by the consumer, allows low frequency sounds from the main speaker channels to be re-directed and reproduced, at relatively low levels, on the dedicated low frequency 'Sub' speaker. So, what used to happen quite a lot in those early 5.1 mixes of video games was that the entire master sound mix was 'sent' to the LFE as though it were an aux channel – which meant that the low frequency effect was continually blasting out the low frequencies from the game. To compound the problem, this was also in the days before loudness standards were adopted throughout the industry, and so the LFE channel was continually received sounds that were peaking at 0dBFS – far beyond what the LFE channel was designed to reproduce on a long-term basis. In addition to this, sometimes specific LFE sounds were authored and sent exclusively to the LFE – for example sweeteners for explosions or gun shots that occurred regularly in the game. However, the main issue with this sweetener approach for principal sound categories was that any such exclusive LFE content would be removed from the down-mix to stereo and not included at all – so that when played on anything other than a *n*.1 system with an LFE, for example on headphones or stereo TV, the game mix sounded thin and weak without the low frequency sweeteners, which usually carried all the power and impact of the sounds designed.

The more sane and general approach today is that the LFE is reserved for very special, rare, highlighted and extreme moments – and even then, low frequency sound is still present in the main channels. One of the most simple and clean approaches is to leave out *any* discreet sound for the LFE entirely, and simply rely on the Sub crossover settings on a home receiver, to re-direct any low frequency from the main channels down to the Sub. This way you will have a reliable and predictable down mix for stereo and surround with the same low frequency content across all endpoints.

33 Building the mix

Mix-as-you-go: built-in to integration

A game is in many ways exceptionally different from a motion picture in terms of how it is produced, and therefore the mixing opportunities and technologies have adapted to match those production realities. However, the approach to the *end result*, of shaping and presenting a coherent interplay of sound to an audience, is identical. The many various milestones and gates through which a video game has to pass through on its way to the gold master disc (First Playable, Vertical Slice, Alpha, Beta and so on) all demand that some semblance of a good mix is present at all times in order to be able to convey that the dialogue, music and sound are all doing what they are supposed to throughout the development process and that the game is coherent to reviewer and playtest audiences.

While I have up to this point focussed a lot on the final balancing of a mix, the condition of the mix *during* development is also an extremely important aspect of ongoing game development. Mixing can actually begin at the very earliest moments, as you set up the project in your audio engine, indeed probably even sooner than setting up the audio engine, as you develop *ideas, the anchor* and *priorities* in the concept phase. Thus, setting up the *idea* of priority, and then building the structure and hierarchy in the game engine to reflect that idea is something that arguably needs to happen even before you get a sound to play back in the game.

Mixing as you go is not an approach that in any way foregoes the notion of a final polish pass, and neither does it remove the need for time dedicated to a final mastering mix at the end of production. However, it is something that should go hand in hand with, and feed directly into that process as a whole. Likewise, you cannot *defer* all the mixing decisions until the end of the project, simply due to the fact that as you make the game, you will need to shape, review and iterate on the content and priorities continually – this of course includes pre-mixing and overall mixing passes – and every sound designer and implementer involved in putting sound into the game should be making mix decisions that express the sound at the correct hierarchies of importance. If ambience is too loud and preventing a player (in play test or review) from hearing the more important elements of navigation and story comprehension, for instance dialogue, or waypoint guiding attractor sounds, it needs to be fixed quickly. Equally, perhaps if the music is not loud enough to carry the excitement and emotion of the gameplay moment, then the mix will need to be adjusted accordingly. Ideally these kinds of elements would be checked before any kind of important play test or team review, but given that major reviews happen almost continually in the game development process, it is necessary to always have a functional mix that is at a minimum able to articulate the main priorities of the experience. Even if the mix is rough and awkward, it should at least be driven by our 'what is the most important thing' principle – simply meaning that the most important thing *should always be the most important thing*. If we hear almost no ambience at all, but we hear the dialogue that tells the player where to go, then the mix is functionally covering the right bases. You may receive a note that there 'is no ambience in the game' from the reviewers – however, this is a *minor* note, and much better than receiving the *major* note about not hearing the dialogue and thus players not being able to complete their objective.

Small subcomponents, like weapons, can have their own mini pre-mixes and indeed will need to be finessed to a point where they are sounding as they should during reviews and play tests. This is so that the players and reviewers can adequately evaluate those features, including the sound, but most importantly evaluate the *game* from an overall feel and feedback standpoint. A small handgun, for example, may have many layers to the sound design, all of these individual elements must be sub-mixed and prioritised together so that each is audible to the correct degree, and not too overpowering or too underwhelming. If individual sounds are very quiet so that they are effectively inaudible due to the playback of other sound layers, then those sounds should likely be removed completely, as they are not adding anything. *Subtraction and removal* are fundamental approaches to mixing; indeed, they are the driving principles behind the very idea of mixing. If there are dynamics that occur over time to the weapon sound, then these should also be mixed, for example, the rotation servo sound of a spinning drum could heat up with continual use, and the pitch and volume could slightly increase as you continue to hold the fire button. These dynamic, diagonal elements of the sound design will need to have their sub-mixes express these micro-narrative shapes in a satisfactory way in order for the feature to be evaluated correctly. As such, the feedback that I give as a director when reviewing any element of a game, will almost always include notes on the shape of the sub-mix of each element, especially because we want to apply our ideas of priority and importance to the player from the earliest moments of feature development – from the largest scale of priority, down to the smallest detail. The mix, or relative volumes of all the elements, is not something that can simply wait until the end of the sound design and implementation process, it must be built into the thinking and design of the feature from the very first moments of implementation.

If these kinds of issues get deferred to the mixing 'phase' at the end of a major milestone, or even to the final pre-mix of a game you are going to eat into all your valuable and scarce mix time at the end. I would argue that these kinds of small bugs and issues *need* to be resolved as a part of the features or maps that are being approved as they go, most especially towards the L3 stages of audio quality. This is so that by the time you reach the final mix stage you are not overwhelmed by focus on fixing minute details of small features – once again, the final mix phase should be as fully focussed as possible on making minor *global* tweaks and adjustments to the *overall shape* of the experience.

Spatial approaches to the mix

In the coming age of spatial audio, whether that is speaker-based home theatre with various numbers of surround channels, or whether it is a run-time binaural image that uses an individually measured HRTF scan of the player's ears and head delivered over headphones, there is an increasing emphasis on the immersive and spectacular use of 3D sound in the audio mixes of video games. It is a significant aesthetic gearshift that affects all food-groups of sound, and many new approaches and experiments will certainly become playable in the coming years.

Video game audiences have the distinct advantage over cinema audiences of being '3D native' (or spatial native) – having become already familiar with navigating and *reading* 3D spaces in games for the past 30 or so years. This 3D-ready audience is in distinct contrast to cinema audiences who have maintained their fixed listening and viewing positions in both theatrical and home settings. And, even though we have seen an explosion in the amounts of surround channels beamed towards cinema audiences over the last decade, the spatial mixes being authored for movies, even in blockbuster action titles, have on the whole remained reasonably conservative in their use of the available height and surround channels. I think this will change over time, and that this transitionary period into the new expansive spatial story worlds of movies that live *beyond* just the screen is already, slowly, starting to happen. The initial reluctance is, I feel, mainly down to the idea that persists since the earliest days of surround sound, the very thing that keeps the sounds focussed to the front and centre, that any distraction from the *screen in front of the audience* is considered a big problem. Of course, some directors are already excitedly experimenting with this newly widened immersive space seeing it is being available for them to create rich, immersive story-worlds beyond just the screen, Alfonso Cuarón's 'Roma' being a rather beautiful case in point. However, these mixes have come under criticism from other film sound mixers who prefer to approach the new listening formats, in theatrical settings at least, from the established notion that a distraction from the screen, is a distraction from the *film*, and that non-sequitur, offscreen sounds in the mix, have the effect of taking the audience *out* of their story immersion.

In video games, while sound from offscreen can still be considered distracting, the audience does not have these same limitations. For the most part, if a sound is heard behind or above the player's field of view (in 3D games), they can simply move the camera to look at the source of that sound, and then, if desired, navigate their character in that direction to investigate what made the sound. Arguably this encouragement of exploration and navigation of the space is built on this notion that an offscreen sound will *cause* the player to go and investigate its source. In design terms, these categories of sound are often referred to as 'attractors' and refer directly to attention-grabbing 3D sources of both sound and dialogue.

Given the ready expectation of the audience to explore and engage with a rich 3D world, the scope for the amount of spatial sound to be used is much wider. Aesthetically speaking, immersive spatial audio is not a revolution for video games that requires fundamental changes in design thinking, but simply another step, albeit a big one, in the same journey that has already been established through use of 5.1 surround, or 3D point source sounds located in the stereo field that pan around based on where the camera/listener is pointing. The revolutionary element of spatial audio for audiences is the *accessibility* and delivery of truly immersive and convincing *binaural* experiences to the mass market through headphones. In the past, what prevented audiences from enjoying *fully* immersive sound was the expense associated with acquiring a surround sound AV and speaker system and having the space available in the home to install it. Today, with the ubiquity of both Soundbars and HRTF binaural sound delivered over headphones, these environments rich in spatial information are now more accessible than ever.

Placing increased emphasis on being able to accurately locate threat locations from offscreen sound, as well as encouraging vertical exploration of physical 3D spaces, no longer limiting players to mostly flat planes, becomes much more feasible, opening up a lot of design opportunities. I also expect, in order to maintain the fidelity and clarity of these spatial mixes, an increased emphasis on uncompressed audio in video games. Uncompressed, PCM source wave files at their highest quality, rather than the compressed and decompressed versions of these sounds, would ideally be what is used to drive 3D spatial mixes, especially in the binaural realms. As game memory increases, and disc access bandwidth becomes less of an issue with solid state drives, this all become more possible. One of the reasons I am optimistic and excited about the potential of uncompressed audio is that the higher frequencies in positional sounds serve to *localise* spatial effects far more accurately. So, for elements that are incredibly important spatially, like enemy gunfire location, some of these threat elements could be implemented using uncompressed PCM at the highest sample rates to increase their *positional effectiveness* is the mix. Additionally, with all the optimisation afforded by mixing techniques like pre-culling and HDR being used to limit the amount of sound voices that are even going to be playing concurrently, the amount of sound needing to be decoded and played simultaneously also drops much lower.

These resulting 'super clean mixes', more prioritisation, less clutter, emphasised design focus on 3D localisation, and the possibility for uncompressed assets to be used – while providing a more richly responsive 3D experience for the audience, will also have the pleasant side effect of positively impacting CPU performance.

Given this new emphasis on the spatial mixes of video games, whether in the triple-A or within mobile and 'Indie' spaces, the attention to detail needed in designing and down-mixing that content, to work seamlessly on any endpoint, must also receive the appropriate increase in planning, budgeting and awareness across disciplines.

The final step: mastering

The most important way to think about mixing overall is that the mix should be readable for the player, regardless of what platform, or audio endpoint, they choose to play on.

Ideally, the planning and execution of a dedicated mastering step, in which the many potential endpoints that the game will filter down to, will be addressed at the very end of the post-production mixing process.

Once you have mixed the entire experience in the highest possible speaker configuration, you can take a step back to make adjustments to the ways that the mix is folded down into other endpoints that accommodate less speakers, or different dynamic ranges. This way you can control and reduce, if desired, the amount of sound folded in from the surround channels to the stereo-only channels for example. Only by first understanding how that experience feels at the highest speaker configuration can you begin to understand what elements of that mix will need to be adjusted to create a similarly exciting, immersive and dynamic version of the same game experience in 7.1, 5.1, stereo or even mono.

Similar consideration must always be given to dynamic range, especially if you are mixing in a calibrated mix theatre at reference levels as the amount of dynamic range that is available in this environment is far higher and more precise than will be available for players at home in a regular living room over TV speakers. It is therefore prudent, once again, to make available for players, a few dynamic range options, in the sound menu, that take into consideration some of the more common playback environments that the audiences for games will likely encounter – such as headphones, or TV speakers. If a player has a high-end home theatre, then the final mix can be presented exactly as it was made in the calibrated mix theatre. However, some compression and limiting can, and almost always should be, made available through these dynamic range options. This is so that players in more noisy home environments, who will not be able to hear the quieter elements of the mix, therefore don't miss out on much of the storytelling occurring in ambient or distant sounds when playing in those environments.

The mix should always be readable and understandable for the player in their environment, so the more tools and options that you can give in the sound options menu, the better chance that the player will be able to adjust some of those options to improve their experience. The worst thing that can happen is that you ship the game with a single mix, no options to adjust any levels, at a single fixed dynamic range, mixed on a perfectly calibrated mix stage… this would mean that the mix you have made, and by extension *the game that you have made*, will only be fully enjoyable by a player in a perfect, calibrated home-theatre environment.

34 Planning and surviving the major milestone and final mixes

As with anything, early planning for your mix at the various critical moments of the project is extremely important in terms of project management and tracking. The time allotted to your mix should be red-lined by production so that it is not considered a 'nice-to-have' time buffer that other disciplines can eat into when they become late. This is the most common form of de-prioritisation that occurs *against* mixing when in the final stages of video games development.

The concept of a rigid mix that slides along the schedule, rather than contracts, is essential to communicate to your production team. Even once your schedule is planned, you will need some strategies to be able to focus on just the mix alone, and not be diverted by all the other chaotic requirements that start to occur at the very end of production. Protecting that time and focus, by making sure you have delegates on the sound team ready to step in to fight fires on your behalf, is also critical to success. Again, it is essential that you plan, as early as possible, the time to author the master mix and the subsequent mastering. You will realise that this requires some scheduling prowess, healthy quantities of good will and constant co-ordination with the production team.

Milestone mixes

In terms of leading and learning from early dry runs and prototyping, there is no better way to model and prepare for the final mixing stage of a game than by attempting to emulate that on a smaller scale for your important qualitative milestones. Milestone mixes are a great rehearsal for the final mix, and you should gradually start to take each mix more seriously, in terms of both your mixing approaches, focus and your scheduling granularity as the end approaches. Having some completely separate, non-dependant mix-only milestones, like achieving loudness targets for all the maps that have final dialogue, should also be considered.

Planning and executing the final mix

The on-the-ground logistics of a final mix can be quite different from what you imagine they might be. Essentially you will be sitting in a room making qualitative decisions about the overall levels, overall shape and overall priorities of all the sounds reaching the audience. In order to do this, you need to logistically get your mix team, your process, and your development equipment *to* that location.

Workstation

Getting a workstation computer to a mixing room can present various logistical and security challenges. If you are mixing the game in the same town and country as the one in which you are developing the game, then transporting a computer can be done relatively easily. However, if you are mixing the game in another country, you will most likely need to get a computer built to spec in the country of the mix and synced up to your game development depot and version control branches remotely. This can be done if your company has an IT presence in the country where you are going to mix the game (or for smaller studios with smaller projects, a powerful laptop can suffice, as long as it can run the development tools). You will be able to provide the specs as well as securely access the machine remotely, so that by the time you get it to the mix stage, it is ready to plug in and do any final smaller syncs on the day before you are due to start mixing. The mixing facility may also be able to provide a machine to your specs and set it up with remote access ahead of time so you can sync the content before arriving. The IT department will be essential in planning and co-ordinating these logistical elements, so discuss the plans with them especially early.

Development kits

In a similar way to getting your computer on site, you will also likely need to arrange the presence of dev-kits if deploying and developing on console. This can also prove challenging as they are not usually things that you are legally allowed to take out of the development studio. Often this will need to be arranged, again in co-ordinating between the country of origin of your mix, with either Sony, Microsoft or whoever is lending you those development kits. The kits, once arranged, can be couriered to the mixing stage, and again, can be remotely set up from your development location prior to your arrival. Another thing you will need to do is make sure that the dev-kits have the latest SDK installed and ready to go, so you are not wasting time doing this long set-up process when you are supposed to be mixing the game. This all needs to happen as far in advance as possible – and again, leaving at least one day before you are due to start mixing the game, to set all this equipment up, plug it into the monitoring systems being used and make sure that things like wireless controllers can work well through the thick walls of the machine room where the devkit will need to be located (development kit fans can be far too noisy to keep them in the mixing room itself). One note here is that remote cloud-centric game development, whereby the instances of the game being built are server-based, rather than running on an actual development kit in the physical location itself, presents great improvement opportunities for mix logistics.

Network

Making sure that your development computer and the dev-kit are on the same network and are able to talk to one another enabling you to push the build from the PC to the kit, as well as connect audio tools to the game is something that needs to be tested and debugged prior to mixing. Similarly, the VPN connection to your version-control environment remotely to the development studio needs to be thoroughly tested and set up – as does copying cooked hourly or daily builds over to the mix stage computer location. Connection speeds should ideally be as fast as possible for these kinds of transfers, and you should check with the IT technicians at the mixing facility to make sure that your traffic is prioritised during certain hours of the day when you will be sending or receiving important data. One day on site may not be enough to wrangle all the issues involved with setting up a remote development environment on a mix stage, so keep that in mind when planning and booking time on the mixing stage.

You may also need to access all the DAW sound sessions and SFX libraries that you have back at the development studio, but this access will be remote via VPN from the mix stage. Setting up secure VPN to do this is another essential layer to a flawless remote mix. You never know what data you are going to need to open up and re-render during the course of the mixing process, so you should endeavour to maintain continued access to everything.

The advantages of taking a game offsite to focus on the final mix far outweigh these logistical elements, and if they are planned for and tested in advance, you can run an entirely smooth remote post-production mix. At such a critical time at the end of a major milestone, or even as you are just about to ship the game, the need for this isolated focus and calm are more essential than at any other time in the production of a video game.

Team focus

This is the moment in the development of the game's soundtrack where the many collaborative voices and opinions involved in creating the game need to be narrowed down to a very small group. This group is the one or two people who can understand, articulate and implement large scale critical mix decisions about the various food-groups, in co-ordination with the appropriate contextual knowledge, in terms of *what is the most important thing* in the game at each particular moment of story and gameplay. The final mix team should be reduced to two or three focussed and trusted experts who together will be able to carry the game across the finish line, and who will be able to deliver it in the time scale that has been agreed. Doing the dry run mixes at major milestones will also allow you to understand the personalities, metrics and time involved in taking an unmixed and unpolished part of the game and getting it to a great sounding and polished final state. These rehearsals and dry runs will provide invaluable data points in determining, and also in further convincing your production team about the amount of mixing time, and the importance of the mix, required for your particular project. Making the shape of the game clear and understandable for the audience is something that requires specialist knowledge of both the game itself, and of the processes used in the game's mix – understanding which systems are doing what to the sound, and which technical elements will offer the best solution in each particular mix situation.

These are all undeniable pressures that you will face towards the end of a project or milestone, and into which you will need to create and maintain the physical and political safe space where your team can make these decisions. This is another reason why leading with the idea of continual mix passes, all the way through production, executing and practicing what they are like, and refining who is involved, is essential to delivering a successful mix pass at the end of production.

35 Leading with the mix

The first and last thing you think about

Last things first

Mixing can, and arguably should, be one of the first things you start to plan and think about on a project. My approach with the production team is to always begin at the end when looking at a schedule and work backwards from there. The first thing we will do is establish the desired ship date, and then start to build the entire production schedule *backwards* from that date, considering each of the four food-groups of sound and their dependencies, beginning with the mastering step, final mix and backwards to the beginning from there. So, in the end, the mix is always the first thing that we begin with, and it usually takes the shape of a two- or three-week reserved block in the schedule for a triple-A game. At this early point, I might even start to gather some bids and quotes from eternal mixing stages just to start things off and get the topic on a serious tone and firm footing. Once we have budget assigned and time pencilled in, we can continually demonstrate, through milestone mixes, that this is a serious and non-movable stage in the final days of the production, one essential to the team hitting their ship date. Of course the time and the timing of the final mix stage may be adjusted, and by all means this may not even be necessary for the kind of game you are developing (for example a game-as-service in which the title updates continually and 'ships' on a short five to six weeks' cadence). This may only require and allow a few days of mix time towards the end, but even with a release cadence as short as this, the planning for the mix time must be so very precise that it may be down to the hour, rather than the day, in terms of planning and execution.

Aside from the production focussed planning and preparation, aesthetically you can begin to approach each of the other three food-groups of the game's audio track by testing them as a whole together, rather than as three siloed food-groups that will eventually 'get together' only at the end. Understanding how much storytelling and player feedback can be handled by each of the three areas of voice, music and sound, is a way of thinking about these mix relationships, and by limiting only one of the three areas of sound to have the spotlight, you can begin to create a good shape to your mix, and game experience, early on. As soon as you start to prototype elements or features, you are always going to be thinking about the mix of the food-groups involved in those elements – even if you are putting together a test, trailer or concept work in a DAW for a video based presentation, you will be making mix decisions about the game's content you are showing and what is being foregrounded and when. This hands-on familiarity with the sound material of your game's universe, will teach you some of the 'why' answers in how to execute the mix for the final game.

At the beginning of a project, you might start thinking about the various audio output options, and user-controlled accessibility elements you wish the player to have 'mix' control over. Once you start to understand what kind of game you are making, you can start to make even more assumptions and do more research into the target audience for the genre and for the devices you are going to be supporting. Quite early on, every game will naturally start to lean heavier in certain directions than others in terms of mix options (audio options in the sound menu) and requirements. A game without dialogue, for example, will need to have some other kind of anchor element against which every other sound group can be balanced. This anchor element may become a volume slider in the sound options for the player.

Thinking early about 'mix moments' where one category of sound carries the overall experience and then hands over to another is a leading with the mix mind-set. Even a first story treatment or script overview can start to be annotated with your notes about the four food-groups, and about the game's 'music only', or 'stillness' moments and so on.

Showcasing the mix and the mixing approaches to the team is also another area where you can inspire and lead in terms of demonstrating some of the systems and philosophies to the priorities and hierarchies of meaning that are being presented onscreen. The use of MIDI control surface technology, whereby a surface such as a Mackie Control is hooked up to the audio middleware to control volumes of sound groups and busses (for example Wwise or FMOD) at runtime, can inspire and open up distribution of these kinds of control surfaces to *other* disciplines on the game team. Thinking about more general game engine tools and shortcuts can be mapped to any MIDI control surface – meaning that *any developer*, whether they work in lighting, animation or game design, can make use of faders, knobs or buttons mapped to shortcuts in their own work routines and processes.

Mix quality assurance

Speaking with and introducing some of your thinking and ideas about the mix and sound priorities in the game to the testing department is also important. The more that the QA department understands about the approaches, sound options and endpoints you will be mixing for the better the QA team will be able to plan to regularly test these things. The amount of different mix endpoints available can make the number of play-throughs and testing plans more complex and lengthier. The game should ideally be played through in its entirety on every single endpoint, with any notes and issues logged prominently – this mix attention should also be made for every localised version of the game as the mixes could vary quite considerably without the knowledge of the main mix team who will only be working only on the default language of the game. Fortunately, if everything has been premixed well, in terms of broad dialogue levels, and methods for matching the loudness levels of each dialogue file in the default version to its localised counterparts then the loc mixes should also inherit the master default mix. Thinking about these kinds of matching systems, and the kinds of communication, connections, dependencies and relationships with the QA team, early on can be a huge help.

Being able to put into place some of these ideas or proposals ahead of time will reduce the pressure on needing to build or manage these kinds of systems and relationships during the end of the project, when 'the mix' is traditionally thought about. It will also give you good foresight into when certain things really need to happen. These conversations may accelerate or raise the priority level of purchasing equipment ahead of testing, such as Dolby Atmos AV systems or home theatre setups, as well as either building or assigning dedicated audio rooms in the QA area for focussed audio testing to take place. Early planning may also highlight the need for growing audio *expertise* within the QA group, especially in terms of understanding the sound from the consumer standpoint, and having the input of the QA team on often overlooked areas, like the wording used in the naming of audio options for the player, is extremely valuable as things start to move through production and towards shipping. Drawing a visual map of the supported endpoints is always a great way to break the ice, and by having and continuing these discussions, allowing everyone to see and understand how the audio will reach the various audiences of the game, this will be a positive advance step in getting ready for the end of the project.

The new post-production: 'true' post-production

Leading with sound is essentially a migration of creative audio from the very end of post-production, where time is limited, pressure is high, and only the most critical things will ever get to be achieved – to the beginning and middle of projects.

To use a gardening analogy, it is the process of *seeding* opportunities, ideas and solutions for sound in the concept phase, *nurturing* them throughout production, all with the express purpose them of *flowering* in post-production. Post-production work is still critical in making everything that has been grown in the garden of sound be at its best.

Post-production then still has its critically important place for sound: even with much more being done earlier, you cannot *polish* until right at the end. It is the focused role of post-production sound to tie up all the loose ends, ensuring that everything is locked down and approved. By having more creative and iteration time up front, we now absolutely *need* the post-production time to finish and polish that work. It is the crucial final step in the realisation onscreen of everything you've been working on.

This is the importance of carving out specific time to go into a specific room and focus on a specific task – this same thing occurs in other disciplines such as colour grading for High Dynamic Range (the HDR *visual* option, not the audio HDR) and so on, and this needs to occur at a very specific time in the game development when the assets are in their final state.

These rigid time and activity blocks associated with finishing the game could arguably be dubbed *true* post-production. They are still creative and technical, though they are *not* heavily iterative, and they are *not* heavily collaborative. they are focussed and precise in their function and are extremely time and delivery centric.

Final mastering and mixing of the game's content clearly fall into the true postproduction area. I use the term 'true' post production, because increasingly in game development, and more commonly now in motion picture production, the area that used to be referred to as post-production now includes major changes to the weighting and fundamental elements of the game or movie, such that they change the interrelationships between core elements in the product. The more fluidity and direction can be applied at the end of the chain of production the further directors and artists and designers have been engaging in tweaking of these elements later in what was 'post-production' – this is now what I would call L3 in our quality level scale. So, now at the *end* of this traditional post-production period, is the new 'true' postproduction period, and it is *here* that your final audio post planning and work must now occur – what we call L4.

True post-production areas, such as final colour grading and the authoring of the final master mix, need to be talked about and showcased with the team as you go through the production, and the more you can share about where you are going to do the mix, as well as who you might be working with on the mix, the sooner the rest of the team will have it in their minds to attend to the work *they* need to in the time they have left. All this is to establish the sense of responsibility across all disciplines about their time hygiene. To encourage the sense that disciplines cannot continue iterative working right up until the day before the game is shipped. The distinction between L3 and L4 is so dramatic in terms of how and what work is done, that it must be openly and clearly discussed at every opportunity.

The mix then is an area that has traditionally been neglected in terms of a holistic and all-encompassing approach for video games. The mix of every game and every genre will be different, and requires different approaches, whether it is a systemic driven mixing hierarchy that pushes the feedback and gameplay, or a narrative driven mixing approach that focusses on character POV, cinematic and story – one mixing approach will not fit every title being produced. So, the 'why' of every mix is something that will be heavily informed by the game itself. The how and when of the mix need just as much careful consideration and understanding that the mix has a place from L1 to L4 in terms of development quality, and will in turn help you plan and understand it from a holistic perspective.

Elevating the importance of mixing to a subject area of video game sound that equals, and often surpasses, the food-groups of sound, music and voice is critically important. At a minimum, understanding that it needs to play an integral part in the aesthetics, planning, scheduling and budgeting of your game is one of the principal goals of this book. The mix touches everything in your game, so you need to have an approach that is strategic, forward thinking and above all else, is a leadership approach.

Part VI

Fade out

The importance of a holistic (four-food-group) vision

Leading with a strong, four-food-group vision for the sound in any game development endeavour is extremely important when it comes to discovering opportunities and finding unique elements for each game. This approach also ensures that sound will be at the vanguard of the team's creative dynamic. Leading each of these food-groups with practical philosophy that embraces creativity, experimentation and collaboration in the earliest phases of concept and production, and then gradually locking down those precious visions into a solidly executed piece of entertainment at the end, is of paramount importance. 'Having your head in the clouds and your feet on the ground' is a great analogy for the creative sound designer, composer or voice designer who is able to conceive, experiment and execute prototypes, in collaboration with other disciplines throughout early production. However, as with everything in video games, this analogy must be *dynamic* – in the beginning, during concept, you can be *entirely* 'head in the clouds', as long as by the end, in true postproduction, you *only* have your feet on the ground.

When you first begin to figure out the shape of the experience, in collaboration with the other visionaries of the various other departments, the approach should ideally explore, or be open to explore, all of the angles that this four-food-group focus allows. Game audio has a truly enormous scope and with this broad remit come equally broad challenges. In order to work as broadly as possible within a team, I believe it is extremely important to work at the project from a high level – as freely as you can – in the earliest moments of conception. And then, once established, build the team, tools, technology and approach aligned with your goals and suited to your culture at the studio, whereby the ownership and long-term visions of all these elements of the soundtrack can take shape and *grow* – and not be overlooked.

Leaving the 'meeting' of the three primary food-groups until the end of production will very often result in messy clashes and painful decisions that need to be sorted out at the final mix stage, where you will need to attenuate and re-adjust or re-design (expensive) elements that were never designed and commissioned with awareness of the other food-groups. Giving every group the exact right contextual information can be difficult as a game is developed, but it is not wise to wait – early exposure, early access, early involvement is the mentality every discipline needs to get used to – and perhaps as a director or lead, your role is to encourage and create the environment in which this can happen.

During the course of these early periods of discovery and experimentation, there will be many opportunities for you to put some of your ideas and potential recipes to the test. At the same time that you are figuring this out, the development environment will be a hive of activity, with concept art, animation benchmarks and other tests being continually done and worked on by the various other members of the team. Everyone's goal is to test and establish vision, or parts of it, and to get something onscreen that can be *approved.* Sound can, and should, play an integral role in those processes as much as it can, and there are so many opportunities to do this when you talk with the team – ideally, nothing produced and shown to the team should be without sound. Doing this regularly gets you and the team familiar with the *vernacular sound of your game* – and by extension this also gets the *audiences* for this material excited – initially your team colleagues in both the sound team and across the wider game team, but also among the various marketing and strategic elements of the business, who will be able to share reactions and feedback about these elements from a very early stage. Feedback is the lifeblood of this continual process of developing the soundtrack of the game. Encouraging an environment in which it is *natural* to give and receive feedback, should be a goal of every game developer, regardless of discipline.

36 Studio culture

A theory of everything

One of the fundamental driving forces behind all the aesthetics, technology and decision making within a development team, is the studio culture. Studio culture grows out of the shared values and priorities of both business and products and is also driven in new directions by the shared passions and beliefs of the team. This is either achieved through strong individual members of that team, or through collective values, groups and movements within those teams. It is always interesting to look at studios with very strong, identifiable cultures, like Media Molecule, or EA Sports and see exactly why they make the kinds of games they make, the kinds of employees they attract and select, the priorities they place on either technology, business or creativity and how the culture itself supports the visions in the games they make. Sometimes it is difficult to even extract the games from the studio culture, and it can often be the case that, within a publisher – who may own several studios with very different cultures – when an IP is transplanted from one development studio, and given to another, that the game style and vision can change dramatically.

The team: a structural design for generalists and specialists

Building an audio team is not an easy task. It is more gardening than architecture. Finding the right people, with the right skills and the right chemistry is the first part – and then it is equal parts planning, luck, training and feedback, as well as *time* for growth. Hiring is one thing, but even before you get into the hiring process, it is absolutely essential to really understand the kind of team and roles your particular project, or studio requires.

The audio department will generally align itself with the overall values and vision of the team within the development studio. The audio team can certainly be in step with, or in advance of (leading) setting these values and directions. The sooner you can start to analyse and interpret what the team's overall values *mean for audio*, the sooner you can start to develop an identity which aligns and resonates with these goals. If you do not understand what the business goals or the cultural goals of your studio are, you should begin that conversation with your studio head, as well as other people on your team. Once you understand the values and vision, you can start to build a team with those overall values in mind.

Multi-team audio approach / centralised audio teams

If you are at a multi-team studio, meaning more than one game is being developed by different teams, and into which full-time sound personnel can migrate from one project to another to best match the shipping schedules of each project, this means you have to look for particular generalist skill sets to match that environment of regular team and project switching.

You will look for generalists who excel at learning new software and new techniques, as well as the new rules and recipes of each project's creative vision. Once experienced, they can work extremely fluidly in these different environments for short to mid periods of time before they begin to tire and become fatigued by various elements of the project. Generalists will often crave a new project, new software and new challenges, this is a strength that needs to be constantly fed and nourished. Specialists on the other hand, will excel at long term tasks with a much more narrow and specific focus. They will continually improve and optimise their particular specialism, not tiring, but gaining deeper expertise and ownership in their specialism. Your team may require a combination of these kinds of people, or it may require one or many 'T-shaped' people, who have a broad range of general skills, but who also carry a deep expertise.

Another approach is to bring in contract generalists, or specialists to work alongside the main team during heavier periods of implementation and production. This temporary contract work suits many audio designers who become freelance, and it is certainly worth building up a reliable roster of these kinds of talents to supplement your team when needed. On the whole though, contractors tend to have specialist skills, such as trailer or cinematic sound designers, or the technical and creative specialisms of re-recording mixers. These are skills that you would need only briefly on a project at a specific moment in production, and you would not need to hire someone full-time. Again, specialism here is a recognised form of expertise dealing with a single element of sound work, someone who has developed efficiencies, techniques and ownership that is coveted by game teams, but not required in-house on a full-time basis.

If you are building an audio team for a single project studio, with a single project vision, this may also require a very different kind of candidate, where sustainable passion and stamina for a particular *genre* may be among the skills you are looking for. Games focussed on specific subjects such as Formula 1 cars or World War 1 weaponry can attract and necessitate these kinds of passionate specialists. So, you may wish to build a team who are going to essentially become specialists of that specific game, rather than specialists of a particular sub-category of sound like Foley or engines.

In order to understand the different kinds of personnel you require, I would at first, very simply, break down the types of audio staff required into *generalists* (the balanced 33% creative, 33% technical and 33% collaborative people from our earlier Randy Thom quote, who can quickly ramp up and down in a variety of roles and operate a variety of different software for limited amounts of time), and *specialists* (those with specific, deep specialisation that applies to a specific type of audio work). From there, you can look at your development and shipping schedule to determine who of these are either temporary *contractors* or full-time permanent salaried *employees.*

37 Game audio studio spaces
Architectural problems in video game sound

A major challenge, and flaw in the architectural imagination of video game studios, is their repeated failure to re-invent the isolated audio 'room' to answer the specific design challenges of video game audio development.

Almost all video game audio facilities, if they have audio rooms, tend to settle on solving the one-dimensional problem of *sound isolation*. As a side effect of this, unfortunately, they also isolate the room's occupants away from the view of their team. This notion is taken directly from the existing models of post-production movie sound, as well as music studio design, where the sound team and work place is as far away from the rest of the production as possible, so the occupants can focus *entirely* on sound. Needless to say, at this point in the book, a focus entirely on sound is not one that should be occurring in game development studios. When it is time to focus exclusively on audio, at the very end of true-post-production, then you can simply rent the space to do that. Meanwhile, the main focus on every development team during concept, pre-production and production, is to collaborate and iterate on content together with the rest of the multi-discipline team. So, rooms then should consider several other factors ahead of acoustic isolation, most important among them being *collaborative prototyping and modelling*.

We desperately need a revolution in game audio studio design, it is long overdue. The spaces in which we work and collaborate need to continually foster this idea of collaboration and exchanges of information *across* disciplinary silos, not reinforcing them with thick walls. The design brief that game audio spaces *should* be tasked with solving, is that the space should be first and foremost a collaborative one – capable of comfortably seating two or more people at a time, fostering a visual and physical belonging to the rest of the team, as well as being embedded inside the team's main space. Another further element of the sound space brief could also be that the 'room' is *moveable*, in that certain sub-species of sound workspaces, like ones used for sound integrators, should be able to physically relocate to wherever the particular team, or cell is located in the building. The elements of acoustic isolation are entirely *secondary* in my view, and can be somewhat, though not entirely, compromised. Whereas the elements of collaboration and visibility on the team are primary architectural elements should not be compromised in the game development environment.

These kinds of problems are so often cast as 'unsolvable', the idea of having something both simultaneously sound isolated and yet embedded on the development team with line of sight visibility and collaborative openness seems impossible. This is a failure of imagination on the part of audio designers who will usually prioritise their own comfort and isolation when 'designing' audio rooms. However, it is precisely these kinds of challenges that continually drive enormous innovation in architectural design – an industry well documented for making use of new innovative materials as well as for considering *human* movement, flow and interaction within the physical space itself.

From a much higher level, we are now heading into a much larger debate about the efficacy and suitability of open plan spaces and offices in general, and whether they are indeed conducive to collaboration and focussed work, or if they are in actual fact a major source of distraction and fatigue.

As with everything in games, if we think about the problem as a dynamic one, rather than a fixed one, we can start to see more solutions. For any team member, being able to oscillate between collaborative spaces and isolated spaces seems to be an ideal solution not just for audio teams, but also artists, designers, producers, directors, writers or indeed *any* of the many disciplines within game development.

One thing we can absolutely agree on is that this oscillation between collaborative social activity and focussed isolation is becoming more necessary, and the more fluid, interchangeable and natural movement between those spaces and those roles becomes, the more we are going to achieve as a team. On many occasions I have 'loaned out' audio rooms to colleagues in other disciplines so that they may focus and work in isolation at certain times on a project. This strongly suggests to me that we need far more of these kinds of flexible isolation spaces and solutions, as bookable resources. Every studio is going to be different, but the amount of focus spaces vs the amount of open plan space should be something taken into account by proactive studio designers. Given the additional necessity of working from home and remote working, equipping these focussed work rooms with good sound systems, acoustic treatment, as well as good microphones with replaceable pop shields and good quality webcams would increase comfort and quality. An array of these work pods could be bookable and used flexibly by *all disciplines* in a game development environment – as well as extending the notion of those pods by having the *core elements* of them available to be sent to and installed at developer's homes. So, accommodating 'remote work' inside the office is also one of the potential shifts needed of current and future development environments.

I feel this is yet another key area where sound departments can *lead* and become advocates – refreshing the ways in which we have traditionally worked. So many of the elements that we in audio refer to as necessities, such as acoustic treatment, calibrated speakers, good microphones etc, should be increasingly considered when putting together *any* kind of working spaces for any disciplines.

By leading with proposals and designs in this area, either when those opportunities present themselves, or by being the ones who step up to propose them initially, audio can improve the quality of the work environment for everyone. As the kind of work we do shifts and oscillates towards focussed work periods, as well as into more individual, acoustically treated video conferencing environments, *away* from difficult to acoustically manage meeting rooms, there is even more scope to develop these discipline agnostic focus spaces.

So rather than seeing audio studios as the only focus for necessary changes in development studio architecture, I see potentially the entirety of development studio architecture as being ready for major change, and that the considerations we would apply for 'good audio environments', will bleed into those general environments for everyone. Whether that is acoustic treatment and the awareness of sound and noise in shared team spaces, or whether it is leading the creation of semi-isolated individual spaces bookable by anyone in the team, and also of course fully usable by audio teams if needed. Wider distribution of 'audio thinking' is something we can always use more of in our development environments.

38 Games are for everyone

Accessibility, options and customisation in audio for gamers

The notion of the user's unique endpoints and the ability to customise or add additional audio cues, such as voice-overlays which enable a full spectrum of players to enjoy the game, is one of the defining features of video games entertainment over that of cinema and theatre. Certainly, the need for inter-activity and feedback in games makes accessibility a more complex element to consider, yet we are continually reminded gamers themselves that often very minor tweaks can enable our games to become accessible to everyone. Accessibility thinking, as demonstrated by studios like Naughty Dog, in which accessibility features are promoted to be one of their fundamental responsibilities, show us that these features in no way impede or compromise the design of the game overall. We make entertainment, and accessibility needs to be an integral part of our thinking, particularly when we claim to be the biggest entertainment medium in the world. With that boast comes an enormous responsibility, because we can *reach* everyone. Audio in particular has huge opportunities to contribute to the increased customisation that a player should be able to achieve over the various elements of the soundtrack. Additionally, being able to render some of the visual elements onscreen through additional layers of audio feedback and guide systems that can be designed, tested, refined and enabled whenever needed.

Customisation of the audio output of video games is something that has long been, and is becoming increasingly, a positive over the audio mix 'options' of other home entertainment media such as streaming movies, whereby you only get the *one single mix* of sounds that the director and mixer authored, with the addition of subtitles, closed captions and described audio. In games, sepa-rate adjustment sliders for music, sound and voice are a standard, and I believe a bare minimum – the granularity of these audio options can be pushed much further in terms of the different sub-groups of sound that we allow the audience to play with and customise to match their personal preferences. Of particular revelation to me was a talk given at MIGS (Montreal International Game Summit) in 2018 by Adriane Kuzminski concerning audio accessibility[1] and in particular a focus on those players, of whom there are many, suffering from varying degrees of auditory processing disorder, whereby the presence of busy and distracting background sound becomes distracting and anxiety inducing.

The kinds of mixes Adriane singled out for praise in games were those that gave control over these seemingly less important background elements of the soundscape, like ambience. So, placing elements of the ambient sound on their own slider, as a subcategory of sound volume, makes it a possibility for someone who needs to reduce or de-emphasise these sounds to do so. Adding this is incredibly simple, perhaps only the work of a few hours. To take this even further, various sub-elements of the soundtrack can be sectioned off with their own volume sliders, such as particular categories of dialogue, like radio dialogue, which may produce more harsh, annoying or anxiety inducing frequencies for certain members of our audience.

Another element for consideration is the ageing gamers in the 50+ category, in which there is increasing need for exactly these kinds of varied accessibility options. Many kinds of sensory impairment increase or manifest with age or in later life, such as accidental damage and hearing loss.

With an increased role for audio at the helm of video game development, and with increased emphasis on exploring the various diegetic and non-diegetic spaces, I expect a similar seriousness around the fidelity and expressive power of non-sound accessibility features to continue to emphasise and develop deeper ways of communicating and *presenting* elements like offscreen sound, for hearing impaired players.

Closed captions that describe some of the *subtleties and emotion* in the sound when they are present in the mix. In a mirroring of the priorities for a game's soundtrack overall, the closed captions should also follow this priority – when subtlety, stillness and ambience is at the forefront of an experience, this can also be communicated to a player through accessible means. Engaging a more *poetic* closed captioning writing style for ambiguous sounds, rather than the strictly informational prose currently used, would be another way to bring the hearing-impaired listener into the more *interpretive* realms of sound and meaning.

Increased fidelity of haptic vibrations in controllers is another such area for extending the reach of sound, being able to play back wave information in stereo to the left and right sides of the controller, so that the player can feel a version of the sound, offers possibility for sound, music and voice to be channelled through that output. Subtleties and ambiguities can still be expressed and felt by *all* our audiences, it just needs that little bit more empathy and leadership on our part to make this a priority.

Individually measured HRTF further expands this idea of personalised endpoints for every player, We all have different biology, and in terms of ear, head and body shape, sound will be perceived differently by *every* listener's brain – in particular this affects spatial audio, but also the overall EQ of a game over headphones. With personalized HRTF, each player can technically experience our 'Master Mix' content exactly how it was intended.

An approach for audio in the realm of interactive entertainment that is geared towards embracing as wide an audience as possible, one where we prevent no-one from being able to enjoy the games we make, is perhaps our biggest responsibility. The existence of the default master mix is essential as a *starting point* for the player to begin to tweak *their* preferred version, obviously we cannot leave the entire mix to the player. This is not what we want our audiences to be doing or focussed on, but we do need those users to have the option of tweaking and changing some of the fundamental categories of sound in the mix, via the options menu – and the more simple and accessible we can make these features in our games, the better for all of our players everywhere.

Note

1 Kuzminski 2019.

39 From invisible to visible

Finding our place, between vision and service

Being an active, forward-thinking and visible part of the game development team is so much more an essential part of the work of anyone in the sound department now than it has ever been. What we inherited in game sound, early on, was a film sound production model forced onto a software development environment. We looked up to the cinematic ideals and promises of post-production sound, and in the end this failed us, because of the continually iterative and collaborative nature of game development. This iterative approach of games is antithetical to the traditional way that motion pictures are made, by first getting approval for a screenplay, bringing on board people and financing to excite investors, shooting that screenplay and then, after shooting, finally polish and post-produce the sound and music at the end. This was the studio model until fairly recently with the advent of CGI and virtual stages, making the process of continually tweaking and changing a movie or TV production eerily similar now to game productions in the way that the visuals and the experience is continually being reformed until the very end. All this means that much of the *creative* work of audio, having traditionally been performed and reserved for the end of production, where it was safely cordoned off into audio post production, now needs to occur and migrate to the beginning and middle of production, where it can get *ahead* of the 'picture' and instead lead the production. One of the most illustrative cases in point is the score of 'Joker', composed by Hildur Guðnadóttir, who worked on creating the music as an emotional reaction to the script, rather than the finished visuals of the film, and therefore wrote and produced much of the music *before* the shooting of the film had even begun. This meant that the actors on set could hear that music, and incorporate much of its mood and emotion into what they did onscreen, even including Joaquin Phoenix dancing to a piece of the musical score written for the movie in one memorable scene – music was used to lead and inspire the actor's performance. This is not the first time that music has been written this early, but it is becoming more common to *think* and work this way, especially as creators seek to get away from some of the creative cul-de-sacs that are imposed by the over-use of temp music and sound, in favour of early collaboration and a leading role for sound and music.

In the end, it should be absolutely clear that, as audio designers, implementers, directors, creators and most importantly as *teams*, we need to be able to understand, work, navigate, express ourselves and our ideas within the changing continuum of the needs and the cultural values of our studios and projects.

We often work in extremely time-sensitive environments and have to deliver quality results under quite extreme pressures, particularly at the back end of deadlines. There is a danger that we take too firm a stance in either one of the following positions... the 'audio as service' position, where anything that is asked of you, will be done and completed without pushback or compromise – where you look only to others for validation of your work. And secondly, the audio auteur stance, where you will not act as a service at all, but instead only as a principal director, in which you will continually question and refine the requests made of your department, but rarely deliver anything in tune with the game. I believe that these extreme stances are never valid, and that in reality we exist dynamically between those binaries, with a combination of these approaches, leaning towards one or the other as necessary to deliver the best results.

As we have seen, right at the end of a milestone, you will need to switch into L4 true-post-production and delivery mode, focussing and locking down. This is the only way everything will get done, on time, to quality. It is also true that sometimes you will need to be the person who says no to a feature, or to a request, based on the interests of good audio – but always remember that *good audio* serves the game. The work of the audio department is a continual dance between these various roles, at various times, in various contexts of production and always to varying degrees and extremes.

Summary

In creative and production driven environments where sound is being continually challenged to rise to, and even exceed the visual elements of a video game, it is important to be able to identify and then seize the unique opportunities that each project presents for sound to become a beacon and to lead the way. Every project is going to present its own unique opportunities in this regard. Whether it is a fresh creative premise where the central character senses and sees the world very differently, or whether it is an opportunity to push one of the major food-groups of sound further to the fore-ground than the others – each project, and each team will speak to us directly about these areas, it is our job to listen to what these games, worlds, characters and stories are telling us and to help show the rest of the team what that is.

Fundamentally understanding *where* in the diegesis the sound, voice and music elements in your games are emanating from is another essential and overlooked element for pushing forward creative visions and exciting content on screen. By using this and the other overarching themes of this book, to *drive* the technical execution of a game's sound with *ideas*, and not be led *by* technology or structural thinking we can answer the 'why' of creative video game sound. We also have the ability to lead a holistic approach with the four interrelated food-groups of sound, categories that all respond to the dynamic and context driven shape of the game itself.

I hope to have inspired you to approach sound decisions and conversations earlier, think more deeply about sound at every opportunity and to frequently take a step back from all the details and the problems, and instead try to see and hear your games, and the ways in which you are making them, through the fresh eyes and ears of your audience. It is also my hope that as we move into the future of entertainment, that the notion of what is and isn't a game will dissolve and become less relevant and less dependent on the definition of whether something is software or celluloid, instead defined simply by the audience's enjoyment and engagement in that entertainment.

Above all else, I hope to have inspired you to begin to lead with sound through any and all means available to you, in whatever creative or collaborative situation you find yourself. Do not wait for the visuals to show you what sounds to explore, or what musical emotions to play with. Do not wait to prototype ideas and share them with your colleagues. Do not wait to start conversations about sound within your teams.

...The problem of art is not simply simulating reality; it is to make something that moves the heart or the mind. If we are to say that video games are the art form of the 21st century, then we need to spend much less of our development time concerned with simulation, and far more exploring matters of the heart and mind.

Bibliography

Altman, Rick. *Silent Film Sound* (Film and Culture Series). New Ed, Columbia University Press, 2007.

Csurics, Michael. 'Tacoma: An Experimental VO Production Postmortem.' *YouTube*, uploaded by GDC, 18 Jul. 2019, youtu.be/sZ8gOm3t40E.

Isaza, Miguel. 'Behind the Art: Randy Thom.' *Designing Sound*, 12 Jan. 2011, designingsound.org/2011/01/12/behind-the-art-randy-thom.

Kelley, Tom, and Jonathan Littman. *The Ten faces of Innovation: IDEO's Strategies for Beating the Devil's Advocate & Driving Creativity Throughout Your Organization*. New York, Currency/Doubleday, 2005.

Kuzminski, Adriane. 'Interacting with Sound: Creating Accessible, Engaging Gameplay.' *YouTube*, uploaded by Audiokinetic, 5 Feb. 2019, youtu.be/UR-vfEO64EE.

Lynch, David. 'David Lynch Teaches Creativity and Film.' *MasterClass* (2019) uploaded by MasterClass, 1 Jan. 2020, www.masterclass.com/classes/david-lynch-teaches-creativity-and-film.

Sergi, Gianluca. *The Dolby Era: Film Sound in Contemporary Hollywood*. Manchester University Press, 2005.

Street, Seán. *The Sound inside the Silence: Travels in the Sonic Imagination*(Palgrave Studies in Sound). Palgrave Macmillan, 2019.

Index

Page numbers in **bold** refer to figures.

9 780367 535872